High Dam at Aswan

THE SUBJUGATION OF THE NILE

Tom Little

Illustrated

THE JOHN DAY COMPANY
NEW YORK

 Published by The John Day Company, Inc., 62 West 45th Street, New York, N. Y. 10036.

Library of Congress Catalogue
Card Number: 65-13754

MANUFACTURED IN THE UNITED STATES OF AMERICA

To my wife
and to Judy and Anna
for their patience

Contents

Illustrations

PLATES (*all following page 114*)

MAP AND DIAGRAMS

ACKNOWLEDGMENTS

Thanks are due to Dr. H. E. Hurst for Plates 1 and 2; to Hamilton Wright of New York for Plates 4a, 5b, 6a and 8; to U.N.E.S.C.O (R. Keating) for Plates 9a and 9b; to U.N.E.S.C.O. (Laurenza) for Plates 10a and 10b; to U.N.E.S.C.O. (P. Almasy) for Plate 11; to *The Forum* (American University of Beirut) for Plate 3a; to the Ministry of the High Dam for Plates 3b, 4b, 5a and 7a; and to the Middle East News Agency for Plate 12.

Preface

The Sadd el-Aali, or High Dam, must be counted among the supreme enterprises of the modern world. This is not simply because of its stupendous size and the difficulty of its construction in the torrid and harsh granite wilderness of Aswan, for man has built big and well in many wild places. This dam is in an ancient land on a river where the record of early civilized man has been written with astonishing clarity. It is the culmination of thousands of years of endeavour to use the Nile for the greatest good of the greatest number and is almost certainly the physical starting-point of a new Egypt.

The dam was also at stake in recent political conflicts inside and outside Egypt and its chequered history is part of the contemporary controversy over Gamal Abdel Nasser's revolution. It was intimately connected with his survival in the struggle against his enemies at home and the foreign powers which resisted his intransigent nationalism. Without the financial demands it made on the State there might not have been the Suez affair, or it certainly would not have happened as it did, and without his stubborn vision the dam would not, I feel certain, be advancing now to its completion, and might not even have been started.

I therefore judged it insufficient only to describe the dam and the building of it. There are, after all, some other rock-fill dams big enough to stand comparison and to describe one is not very different from describing another. I have tried to present the dam in its context: as part of the age-long struggle of the Egyptians to use their river, as a radical development of the lower Nile, as the fruition of many far-sighted people's ideas, as an element in Nasser's survival, as a victim and a victory in his conflicts. Finally there is Nubia and its people and the muck and monuments that will be displaced or lost.

To do justice to the dam would require more than the single

volume I have been able to devote to it. One might dig deeper into contemporary history to find the full meaning of the High Dam in the evolution of politics in and with Egypt; the design of the dam and its modifications, which I hope I have described in sufficient detail to make sense to the layman, is of considerable importance to engineers; the removal of the Nubians from their part of the Nile is in itself a socio-historical study of immense interest; what I have termed the campaign of the scholars in Nubia is worth a dozen volumes and will probably get them; and finally the economist could have much to say of the impact of the dam on the economy of struggling Egypt. One volume is not enough for so many worth-while themes, but for better or for worse I have attempted it.

I am very conscious that I could not do justice to the many people who played important parts in the enterprise, but the truth is that the engineers and technicians who are building the dam, the officials who have moved the Nubians, and the scholars who have salvaged the history of the Nile, would, if named, have filled a volume anyway. If I have mentioned names it is not to recognize them alone, but all those who have worked with them in the enterprise.

A bibliography is hardly possible for this book. The early chapters might reasonably be covered by a hundred or so books about Egypt, and for the rest, the building of the dam, the evacuation of Nubia, and the prehistoric and archaeological exploration by the scholars, I have relied on my visits to the region, my conversation with many people who worked there, and the official reports that periodically recorded the operations. From time to time I have noted references drawn from other sources, but some sources should perhaps be mentioned here. Messrs Hochtief were kind enough to prepare for me complete documentation of their original work on the designs for the dam, which was essential to the understanding of the engineering. The U.A.R. Department of Information produced a number of useful reports on the work, some of which I have referred to in passing, but I am grateful to Sayed Taha Abou el-Wafa, Under-Secretary of the Ministry of the High Dam, who patiently explained to me the progress reports and often brought them up to date in his own handwriting; the interpretation of these reports is, however, mine. Mme Samiha Tawfiq, of Reuters, kept me posted with many press-cuttings about the dam when I was not in Egypt. H.E. Sidki Suleiman, the Minister, gave me time for discussion when he was hardpressed and sometimes visibly tired, and I must thank those of his engineers who showed me periodically over the site, often returning to it with me after they had already spent hours of work there. This was also true of Chief Engineer Gamal al-Batrawy, of Osman Ahmed Osman's Arab Contractors Company, who personally conducted me and explained the progress made at the crucial period when the schedule of work had been restored. Mr Osman Ahmed Osman was himself helpful, as were his staff: notably Mr Ibrahim Farag, at that time his Director of Public Relations, Mr Ahmed Moharrem, at Aswan, and, as many journalists who reported the diversion of the Nile will confirm, the indefatigable Hussein Lutfi. Mr Herbert Addison was kind enough to read the manuscript and was, from his wide experience of civil engineering on the Nile, able to save me from some errors; any that remain are entirely my own work.

It was impossible to look at all the monuments and 'digs' in Nubia; Abu Simbel of course, and Philae, Buhen where a rat – 'don't disturb it, it's a friend' – ate my shoe-laces like spaghetti as I slept in the pottery room, Faras, Kasr Ibrim, in the dog days of summer, Kalabsha, by that time reconstructed near the dam, the temples dismantled by the Egyptians and laid out in numbered stones on Elephantine Island. The essential records of the Nubian campaign were contained in the reports of U.N.E.S.C.O., which reproduced the statements of the Departments of Antiquities of the U.A.R. and the Sudan and of the international panels of experts as well as its own deliberations. I must thank Miss Yvonne Tabbush, of the Paris headquarters, for keeping me supplied with these reports, but to record them by their reference numbers would have made the footnotes look like cipher messages. There are also the volumes of *Kush*, the Journal of the Sudan Antiquities Service, but unfortunately many of the reports on the Nubian campaign which are now emerging from the missions were not available when this book was being written. I must thank Sayed Thabet Hassan Thabet, Director of the Sudan service, for his help at Wadi Halfa.

Finally, a necessary note of thanks to Mrs Peggy Ball of Whitchurch, Oxfordshire, who worked hard and efficiently in typing this manuscript at short notice.

Whitchurch, Oxon.
August 17th, 1964

PART ONE

Prophecies and Politics

The Prophets

In 1700 B.C., the Pharaoh Apophis dreamed that seven fat kine came out of the river and were eaten by seven lean kine that came out after them; and that seven full and good ears of corn growing on one stalk were devoured by seven withered, thin and blasted ears that grew after them. He called an Israelite languishing in jail to interpret the dreams.

'And Joseph said unto Pharaoh, "The dream of Pharaoh is one: God hath shewed the Pharaoh what he is about to do. The seven good kine are seven years; and the seven good ears are seven years: the dream is one. And the seven thin and ill-favoured kine that came up after them are seven years; and the seven empty ears blasted with the east wind shall be seven years of famine. This is the thing that I have spoken unto Pharaoh: what God is about to do he sheweth unto Pharaoh. Behold there come seven years of great plenty throughout the land of Egypt: and there shall arise after them seven years of famine . . ."'

Joseph advised Pharaoh to take up 'a fifth part of the land of Egypt in the seven plenteous years . . . that food shall be for store to the land against the seven years of famine. . . .'

Genesis, Chapter 41

'Si je gouvernais ce Pays, pas une goutte d'eau ne se perdrait dans la mer.'

NAPOLEON BONAPARTE *Mémoires de Sainte Hélène*

'. . . and these gigantic enterprises may in their turn prove but the preliminaries of even mightier schemes, until at last nearly every drop of water which drains into the whole valley of the Nile . . . shall be equally and amicably divided among the river people, and the Nile itself, flowing for three thousand miles through smiling countries, shall perish gloriously and never reach the sea.'

WINSTON CHURCHILL *The River War*, 1899,
writing of the first Aswan Dam project.

'But the High Dam is more than a mute monument of rock on which one may put wreaths of flowers; it is a live, creative monument. . . .'

PRESIDENT NASSER *The Year Book of the U.A.R.* for 1960

CHAPTER ONE

'By Allah, a Mountain!'

One mild March day in 1961 the granite at the first cataract south of Aswan town broke into throaty, spasmodic coughing as twenty tons of dynamite exploded in set pattern deep under the east bank of the Nile. The bright sun was for a time eclipsed by the cloud of rock and dust that seemed to clamber into the translucent air and before it had fallen back to earth three monstrous mechanical diggers crawled clumsily towards the shattered rocks, their scoops poised like the heads of long-necked dinosaurs emerging from prehistory.

Fifteen months earlier, President Nasser, in the presence of many distinguished people called to Egypt to witness the ceremonial beginning of work upon the Aswan High Dam, had exploded the first symbolic charge. There was neither symbol nor ceremonial in the explosions of March 1961; by then the dream of years made their first mark on the face of a wilderness, and the moment was witnessed only by a few startled tourists, one or two curious stragglers from the town, and by the riders of the dinosaurs and the grimy minions who slaved after them.

The monsters nuzzled their sharp snouts into the earth that had lain undisturbed for 20,000 years or more, but for many weeks there was little to show for all their frantic shovelling. The glinting stone lay in piles as though a demented cosmic digger had been at work before, and in this landscape of tortured rock, man's efforts seemed no more than an encouragement of natural chaos. Reinforcements in time joined the mechanical diggers to make a herd of ten, grunting together on the high river bank, and at last they all sank from view in crude holes of their own making. From a promontory one could look down on their noisy, grinding labour, and in the opposite direction see the waters of the placid Nile held by the old Aswan Dam four miles to the north. Men and machines were digging a deep trench in the plateau of the east bank, through which the river would eventually be deflected to leave still water in the natural channel for the founding of the High Dam.

When the dam is completed it will not resemble the existing Aswan Dam, which is a concrete wall pierced by sluices, but rather a solid rib of mountain over half a mile wide at base and well over two miles long, stretching from the granite wall of one bank to the sandhills of the other. A lake as long as England and containing twenty-six times more water than the existing Aswan reservoir will form behind it. This lake could cover every yard of agricultural land in the world and many great dams could be lost in it. For this is among the biggest projects of its kind conceived by man. The Kariba Dam in Rhodesia may hold more water; the Myporo in Japan, the Serre Ponçon in France, the Grand Dixence in Switzerland and some others may be higher; the United States and Russia have massive dams; but taking water, power and mass together few excel the High Dam as conceived. A Nubian remarked as he stood in the chaos of rocks, his eyes fixed in wonder on the hills in which the dam would root itself at the other side of the river; 'A big one, khawaga! By Allah, a mountain of a dam!'

Even before the explosion in 1961, the struggle for the High Dam had been fought by the revolutionary government on many fronts. The country came near to disaster in pursuit of the needed money and its credit in years to come is pledged to Russia for the building of it. Neither risk nor price has been too high for this, the economic corner-stone of the new Egypt. The prosperity and progress of the Egyptian people, the agrarian and industrial plans, the very workability of the co-operative socialist system which is the target of the revolution, are all – in the view of President Nasser himself – dependent on the successful completion of the dam and the great hydro-electric power house to be built alongside it.

The geography and history of Egypt make plain why this is so.

The north-east corner of the African continent is a wilderness of mountain, rock and desert through which the River Nile flows in lonely splendour. Winston Churchill, sweating his way south to Khartoum with Kitchener's army, saw it mirroring the cloudless sky and wrote that it was 'a thread of blue silk drawn

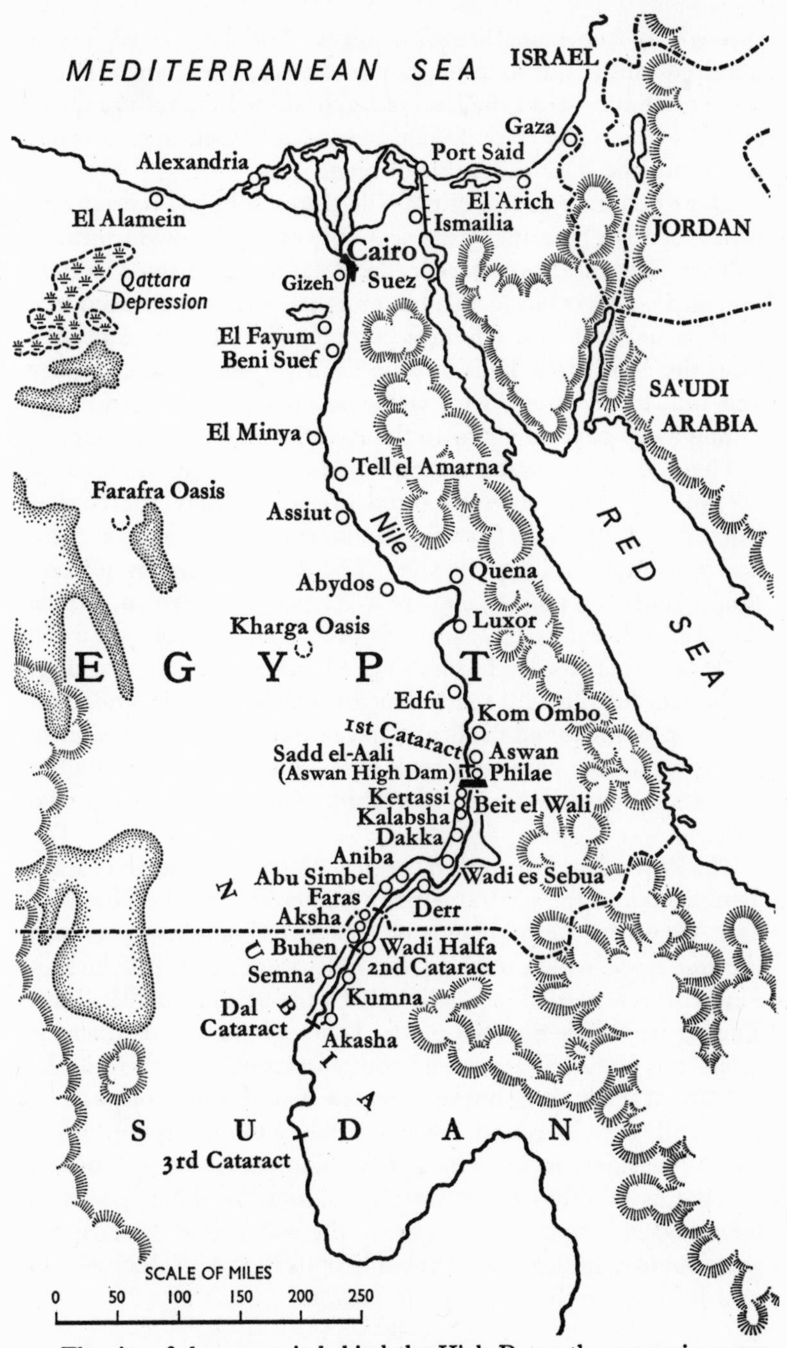

1. The site of the reservoir behind the High Dam: the reservoir covers inhabited Nubia

through an enormous brown drugget'. On the last seventeen hundred miles of its long journey to the sea, not a single tributary enriches it. In all the land of Egypt there is no rain to speak of and without the river it would be a waste land and forsaken by all but the most miserable of men.

The 1,000-mile course of the Nile through Egypt is a narrow valley of reverberating greenness only six miles wide until it reaches Cairo and broadens in the delta to reach the Mediterranean Sea. An orbiting astronaut might see it as a tall palm tree with its head of bushy foliage reaching into a blue sky; seen from the Mokattam Hills outside Cairo, it disappears, slender and still, to the south, with yellow sands on the east and west rolling away beyond vision to the Red Sea and the Atlantic.

There are a few oases, a strip of man-made vegetation along the Suez Canal, and some timid greenery where the coastal fringe gets a little rain from the Mediterranean; otherwise there is only sand away from the river. The area of Egypt is 386,000 square miles but only 15,000 are fit for people to live on. This is the ultimate fact of Egypt. It has been true for more than the 6,000 years of recorded history since Menes, the first known king, dammed the Nile with mud, that the people have depended on the river for meat and drink and have eaten well or gone hungry according to the care they took of it. 'The area multiplies the desolation,' wrote Winston Churchill. 'There is life only by the Nile.'

The White Nile rises on a 6,000-feet plateau just north of Lake Tanganyika in the central African highlands and the Blue Nile and Atbara in the highlands of Ethiopia. Together they form the Nile river, which travels 4,160 miles from its central African source. It is exceeded in length only by the Mississippi–Missouri. The White Nile is steadied by the Lakes Victoria and Albert, is reinforced by its tributary the Sobat, loses much of its flow in the swamps of the Sudan, but maintains a steady supply of water to Egypt all the year round. The Blue Nile sets the rhythm of the river. The rain-bearing winds of the South Atlantic beat on the mountains of Ethiopia in March; in June the Blue Nile is in flood and in August it is, as part of the Nile proper, in rich red spate against the steep eastern banks of its Egyptian channel and overflowing the shallower western slope.

For thousands of years it has behaved in the same way. To the people of the Nile Valley it was the annual miracle that fertilized their parched and scorched lands, and they would pray to the god of the river for the gift of water. When the flood came, it slowly submerged the low-lying banks, soaking the ground and depositing a fine layer of rich silt before draining back to its course and the sea.

The Egyptians learnt early in their history to build low mud walls to hold the water for longer periods in shallow basins. Every year the flood waters submerged the valley, except for small natural or artificial hills on which the villages perched and the peasants lived. This system underwent little change until well into the nineteenth century and about a million acres or nearly a sixth of the cultivated land of Egypt is still irrigated by this system, much as it was in the time of the pharaohs. There are some people who still remember how the countryside west of Cairo was submerged each year in a shallow lake from which palm trees and villages raised their heads.

The need to use the Nile for the greatest good of the greatest number was one reason why Egypt devised the first system of central government known to history, and there were times when a powerful pharaoh would organize irrigation on a big scale. There were man-made canals dug long ago from Wadi Tumilat, between the delta and the isthmus of Suez, as the alluvial bed, deposited there when the Nile flood escaped through it, bears witness. The natural channel from the river to Lake Karoun, in the Fayoum oasis forty miles south of Cairo, was widened and deepened 4,000 years ago, and about 500 years later a pharaoh built a wall around the lake to make it a storage basin for the irrigation of 50,000 acres of lakeside land. The lake must then have 'regulated' the flood in the manner of modern irrigation by reducing its peak and then delaying its fall. The Nasser Government has erected at the High Dam an ancient statue of Om Hotep who proposed the use of the lake for storage and was therefore a prophet of the Nile reservoir system.

In the main, however, the irrigation system was controlled during the greater part of Egyptian history by villages or combinations of villages, whose inhabitants worked in unison to strengthen river banks or dig and clean ditches which ran higgledy-piggledy about the valley at the whim of the villagers themselves or the lie of the land. The flood waters, crowding down the valley on their inexorable journey to the sea, spread themselves over the low-lying ground and it was the task of the farmers to make the straggling margins pause long enough to soak the fields. All their ingenuity was devoted to securing the greatest use of the water, either by drawing it farther afield or by draining a trapped pool from one piece of ground to another before letting the dregs flow back to the river. To achieve the smallest extension of cultivation beyond the limits of the natural flood they had, in effect, by one means or another, to make the water flow uphill.

They achieved this feat about 3,000 years ago with an instrument called the *shadoof*, which consisted of a long bar pivoted between two vertical posts, with a jar at one end and a weight at the other. The jar was lowered and filled at the river by a peasant who, helped by the weight at his end, would lever it out, swing it over the field and empty it into a ditch, watering a precious quarter of an acre by a full day of this back-breaking toil. Later, two other lifting devices were invented. The archimedian screw consisted of a drum, with the screw inside it, mounted between two posts on the river bank and set at an angle of 30 degrees with the lower end in the river, so that a man turning a handle could revolve the drum, lifting the water up the screw until it trickled from the upper end on to the land. Two men taking turns at the handle could water about three-quarters of an acre a day at any place where a short lift was required. The *saqia* consisted of a wheel rimmed with pots set vertically in the water and cogged to another wooden wheel set horizontally over the land. A cow, a camel or a buffalo turned the wheel on the bank, filling the pots as they passed through the water and emptying them into a channel as they swung down again. Five acres a day could be watered in this way.

These simple instruments, still to be seen at work on the Nile, are evidence of the obsessive need of the Egyptian farmer to get as much from the river as possible. They enabled him to lift the water above its normal level, and sometimes to get a second crop from at least a part of his land, and therefore they were primitive answers to the fundamental problem of Egyptian agriculture and the germ of the system of perennial irrigation perfected by British engineers and hydrologists sixty years ago. The simple *shadoof* was, in its time, almost as wonderful and important as the High Dam will be tomorrow.

When Mohammed Aly became viceroy to the Turkish Sultan in 1805, Egypt was in a sorry condition, and he set his people to work at once cleaning ditches and digging new ones. He required industries and an army to further his ambition and both required more money than the products of his agriculture then provided. When French advisers proved that Egypt could cultivate excellent cotton, which Europe wanted and would buy, Mohammed Aly decided to grow it, and by this decision he gave new and permanent impetus to the idea of perennial irrigation, for cotton requires water in the late spring and summer, when the Nile is low.

To grow enough cotton he required more than canals, ditches and water-lifting machines, and he was at last persuaded by two engineers, a Belgian and a Frenchman, that a barrage should be built at the apex of the delta just south of Cairo in order to hold a head of water high enough to supply canals and ditches to the north[1]. Although he did not see the completion of the barrage, which was, in any case, a faulty construction that stood unused until the British came to Egypt, Mohammed Aly set the pattern of modern Egyptian agriculture by his decision to build it and his introduction of cotton as a cash crop. His grandson, the Khedive Ismail, driven by the double demands of ambition and creditors and by the high prices cotton was fetching in Europe as a result of the American Civil War, improved the system he inherited, and when cotton prices slumped, he cut the Ibrahamieh Canal from Assuit in Middle Egypt on a northward course along the west bank to the delta and introduced sugar cane.

The British occupied a bankrupt state when Ismail abdicated in 1882, and they were driven by international creditors as

[1] A barrage, unlike a dam, has no storage function; it arrests the flow until the water is high enough to flow into canals and ditches above the natural channel.

importunate as they were numerous and powerful, to concentrate for the first decade of their rule on raising the national income in order to pay its debts. The effective management and extension of the system introduced by Mohammed Aly was the only means of doing so. Sir Colin Scott-Moncrieff, who was brought with other engineers from British India to take charge of irrigation and public works, first made good the work of Mohammed Aly by repairing those faults in the barrage that had prevented its use for more than forty years and by redesigning the canal system by which the water held by the barrage could be efficiently used in the delta. By 1890 the barrage could hold a head of 13 feet, far more than had been intended when it was designed.

The British engineers then began to devise plans for storing some of the surplus flood water for use in the summer, and the outcome of their planning was the first Aswan Dam.

The behaviour of the Nile required a structure of a type then new to the world, for it is the peculiarity of the river that it sends its flood at the height of the summer heat and drought, when other dry, torrid zones are desolate; as, indeed, is the Aswan region outside the narrow valley. The proposed Aswan reservoir dam had to allow free passage to the early flood, laden with its fine regenerating silt, and then trap the clear water at the end of the flood season for use some months later. In this way it could maintain the value of the flood to the basin lands in the period of ordinary inundation and make water available for second or even third crops in the season of low water. It was two things at once: a massive concrete wall and, by the use of its numerous flood gates, a weir able to control the river in spate, and not, as in ordinary weirs, at low water.

The dam was an epoch-making event. It stretched two miles across the valley and rose nearly 90 feet above the river bed – 'a colossal barrier, formidable, a veritable mountain of granite', as M. A. B. de Guerville described it in 1905.[1] The 1½ million cubic feet of masonry that went to its construction were laid on solid granite 30 feet below the crumbling floor rock, involving a foundation problem which the first design had avoided as much as possible by choosing the path of the best rock, in three dis-

[1] M. A. B. de Guerville, *New Egypt*.

connected sections in the shape of an elongated and angular 'S' bridging the five stormy channels of the Aswan cataract. It was the international commission of experts called to judge the scheme who favoured a straight unbroken wall, cutting the first three corners of the original scheme and giving the dam an austere splendour. Time was to prove that it did no damage to the dam's strength and stability and it gave the Egyptian Government a dam capable of impounding twice the quantity of water contracted for. As the world applauded the great feat, only William Willcocks, Director of Irrigation Studies for the Egyptian Government, mourned over the absence of a cornice, for not even the persuasion of this most stubborn of men could win the approval of the international experts for the pharaonic decoration he believed his dam deserved.

The dam which made Egypt rich for a decade, could not exorcize the spectre of poverty altogether, and such was the inexorable pressure of population that even before it was finished there were plans to heighten it. Sir Benjamin Baker, an engineer of undisputed authority in the matter, who led the international commission on the Willcocks plan, examined the river for the site of a new dam, but just before he died in 1907, he pronounced in favour of heightening by a method which amounted to 'welding' fresh masonry to the wall. (Years later test engineers found the bonds stronger than the original construction.) The heightening was completed in 1912 but the dam was raised again in 1933 to hold one and a half cubic miles of water. This is the dam as it is now seen at Aswan.

The modern system of irrigating Egypt took shape from the dam. The lake behind stored water from the flood to supply the valley in the low season; the Mohammed Aly barrage at the apex of the delta raised the river to the level of the three main canals, two roughly parallel with the Rosetta and Damietta branches of the Nile and one on a line due north through the middle of the triangle; and these main canals were equipped with 'regulators' controlling the supply of water to a carefully laid-out network of irrigation canals and ditches.

Development took place consistently along these lines. Now, going down-river from the dam, there are at regular intervals the Esna, Nag Hammadi and Assuit barrages, with their main canals drawing-off behind them. The Mohammed Aly barrage, after fulfilling its purpose for half a century, is replaced by barrages on the Rosetta and Damietta branches and serves only as a picturesque, monumental road bridge set in one of the loveliest gardens in Egypt. There are more barrages on the two arms of the Nile culminating in the Edfina near the Rosetta mouth.

The control of water through this elaborate system is the work of an experienced and highly efficient Irrigation Department, which has for many years been entirely staffed by Egyptians. It is they who direct the flow all the way from the Aswan reservoir to the distributing canals, which water about twenty-five or thirty acres each. The greatest demand for water is made from the end of July to October, the period during which the summer fallow land is planted with maize and the whole area is under crop, but this is the period of the Nile flood, when the only limit on the water supply is the capacity of the brimful canals and the regulators that measure the supply to the distributing channels and ditches. In October, when the winter cereals, beans and berseem cover most of the cultivated land, the demand for water declines sharply, but in about late February, when the river is falling rapidly, the fields need more water than they can get from the natural flow of the river, and the controlled release of water from the Aswan reservoir begins. The winter crops are harvested and cotton and rice, together covering about half the cultivated area, are planted and watered from the reservoir. This, even now, is a time of great anxiety, for the river is at its lowest and the stored water is being steadily dispersed. It is first distributed to the standing crops and only when news comes of the new flood from the upper reaches of the Nile will the Irrigation Department release water to the fallow land in readiness for the planting of maize. At this time there is strict control over the use of water in the fields, for, except in the Assuit and Girga regions where water is pumped from wells for summer crops, the whole area of perennial irrigation depends on carefulness. The meanest farmer grovelling on his acre of land on the fringes of the valley prospers or goes hungry according to the amount of water he can get from Aswan.

The areas of basin irrigation can only grow one crop a year, even though improved methods of using the natural flood have been developed this century. Some farmlands too high to benefit from the natural flow are watered from canals by pumps and *saqias* for the crops planted in August, but it is still generally true that the farmers of the basins wait until October and November, when the flood drains away, to plant their crops of wheat, barley, lentils, beans, chick peas, berseem or clover, and then get no more water. Their crops are harvested in late March or April and the land lies fallow until the next flood.

There is no equivalent area in the world as intensively and skilfully cultivated as the Nile valley in Egypt. Ever since the days of Mohammed Aly, and particularly since the British occupied the country in 1882, every effort has been exerted to provide water for the cultivation of more land or for growing two or more crops each year on land in cultivation. This has intensified the country's dependence on the Nile, and the rain-bearing winds of the Atlantic still do more than man to determine whether Egypt will have a good or bad year. Each year stands on its own; the flood can still come in spendthrift spate to threaten the farms with too much water, or in such niggardliness that the people go short of food, and there is no way of saving the water of the good year for the salvation of the bad.

It was proved in the first half of this century that, excellent though the system is, it cannot satisfy the needs of Egypt. The lower Nile valley is the most densely populated area in the world and every minute that passes another child destined to survive is born. The population that was over 20 millions in 1952 when the Free Officers seized power, was 25 millions a decade later, and looks like being 38 millions in 1982. The very virtues of civilization, the humanitarian mission of mankind, have served only to intensify the problem. Because more babies died in Egypt than in any other country keeping records, doctors worked to keep more and more alive. They fought tuberculosis, bilharzia, trachoma; and when cholera broke out once more in 1947, the world's health services were mobilized to save the population from decimation. The results of these efforts were limited in extent, but a backward view over the decades that measures them against the starting point of progress shows them to be striking enough. In Egypt, however, it was like saving a man from the gallows in order to starve him to death.

Until half a century ago the nation's prosperity could be judged by the number of people who lived in the valley. Left to itself, in peace, with only the hands and harrows of peasants, it was able to support 7 million people, for this was the population at all the best periods of ancient times, whether pharaonic, Greek, Roman or Arab. When Napoleon invaded Egypt at the end of the eighteenth century there were only about 2½ million inhabitants, the end result of centuries of misrule, strife, famine and plague, and at the beginning of Mohammed Aly's reign there were only 3 million. It was not until the seventies, in the time of his grandson, Ismail, that the population once again touched the 7 million mark.

In the short space of time between Mohammed Aly and the abdication of Ismail, the seemingly insoluble problem of Egypt stood revealed: the population grew faster than the fields to feed them, and Ismail left three-quarters of an acre for every inhabitant instead of the acre at the start of his grandfather's reign. It is true that in this period the rigid limitation of the acreage had been broken by the introduction of the perennial system of irrigation, by which five crops were taken off the land every two years, but time was to show that double-cropping was not enough.

The British made Egypt one of the most fertile and profitable pieces of agricultural real estate in the world but they could never make it as fertile as the people who lived on it. When they occupied Egypt in 1882 they brought experienced irrigation engineers from the rivers of India, who applied the Mohammed Aly system with efficiency and extended it continuously. Lord Cromer, the first of the British pro-consuls, said it was the duty of the civilized Englishman 'to extend the hand of fellowship and to raise . . . morally and materially, from the abject state in which he finds them' the millions of native Egyptians at the bottom of the social ladder. He did much for them, but he could not improve their lot in proportion to their numbers. When he retired in 1907, Egypt was in the middle of a boom that astonished the world and made fortunes for landowners and the traders of Cairo and Alexandria, and the country, supporting

12 million people on just under 8 million crop acres of enhanced fertility, was richer than at any time since. The prosperity derived from the Aswan Dam, but by the time the dam was heightened in 1912 the boom was already past. Nothing the British subsequently did kept pace with the population and when the dam was heightened a second time in 1933, providing nearly another million crop acres, there were 5 million more mouths to feed, and only half an acre for each inhabitant. A great part of Egypt's material progress in the last eighty years stems from the work of the British, but the irony of it is that when Egypt secured her independence in 1936, the people were, on the average, poorer than when the British came.

King Farouk's Egypt achieved less than the British. It brought 800,000 crop acres into cultivation before 1952, but, once again, there were another 5 million people living off them; every two acres were supporting seven people instead of the three at the turn of the century, and there was a surplus of 5 million peasants. The lack of land would have brought the country to disaster had it not been for the increased output from the perennial areas, but the point was reached at which new lands and higher yields combined could not keep pace with the population. At last the yields began to level off, because no more could be squeezed from the generous soil, or began to decline because the land was exhausting itself, or, after continuous irrigation, was not being adequately drained. This meant that an increasing part of the national income had to be ploughed back as fertilizers to sustain the vital fertility. In the last quarter of a century it was extremely difficult to enrich or extend cultivated land to any notable extent.

Egypt needed something more than agriculture but all this time the possibility of industrial progress seemed remote. Mohammed Aly tried, without permanent success, to found industries, the Khedive Ismail laid the primitive foundation of an industrial state with roads, bridges, telegraphs, ships and harbours, before he brought the country to bankruptcy, and the British encouraged the building of small factories to meet military needs in two wars: but all this counted for little against the size of the need. The British never contemplated an industrial Egypt and successive Egyptian governments, dominated by conservative rich who preferred to invest in land or houses long after the investment had ceased to benefit the nation, never tried to create one. The reason for neglect was obvious. Except for cotton and some sugar cane for which industries were made, raw materials were lacking or difficult of access, and the people were too poor to purchase industrial products. Above all, there was a shortage of power.

The wealth and sophistication of Cairo and Alexandria were only bright bubbles on the surface of Egyptian society, which elsewhere consisted for the most part of peasants elbowing each other for space to work on the overcrowded fields. There was no shortage of land – great empty tracts surrounded the fretful valley – but there was no more water. Yet, almost every year, Nile water, as precious as gold in Egypt, flowed wastefully into the sea, and the magnificent best of the Aswan Dam could not prevent it.

What is more, because it was able to hold back only a part of this flood, the dam did not necessarily protect the country from disaster. It is true that when compared with the malignancy of some other rivers the Nile is well behaved and even kindly. It leaves its boisterous youth behind in the gorges and canyons of the African mountains, its sulky adolescence in the swamps of the Sudan, and the growling protests of its middle age in the cataracts of Nubia. By the time it has passed Aswan – for man has numbered the cataracts in reverse order, so that the first is last in the river's long journey to the sea – it has achieved the calm of old age. But if its old age is sometimes mean of mood, it can also be generous to a fault, killing with too much kindness. Then it is not starvation that threatens the Egyptians but the relentless surge of the flood on its uncontrolled course to the sea.

There were four serious flood disasters between 1860 and 1880, the worst of which occurred in 1879. Although the river banks had been kept a metre above the previous flood level of 1874, the water broke them above Cairo, swept over the land all the way from Minia to Cairo and re-entered the river at the Rosetta branch in the delta, and it breached the Damietta arm of the Nile to flow unhindered across land to the sea. The population of the valley and the delta scrambled on to the mounds or outwards to the hills lining the valley, and some of them, men, women and children, and their cattle, were drowned, and many more saw their mud-brick houses dissolve in lumpy dark-grey soup and swirl away. Better management and earlier warning prevented a similar calamity in 1887, when the valley became an immense lake, but the people were again forced to camp with their movable property and animals on the desert fringes while their houses crumbled away below them.

There has not been any serious loss of life by flooding since 1880, although the system of canal irrigation makes Egypt to some extent more vulnerable to it than ever because the high banks surrounding the basin lands have given place to canal banks, which are little more than a yard higher than the level of the land and are below that of the river. On the other hand, defence is made easier by modern transport by which men and materials can move swiftly to points of danger. Stocks of stone, timber and tools have been assembled at intervals along the banks, in charge of an engineer who has trucks at his disposal, and the banks are strengthened to minimize the danger of slipping and breaking when they are saturated by the flood water.

The Aswan Dam and its associated systems of defence reduce the danger from high floods by holding water back for the low season, but its capacity is limited and the many safeguards on the river display the persistent anxiety of everyone responsible for controlling it. The losses sustained by another flood like those of 1863 and 1878 would be much greater now because of the development of the country and the increase in population, yet no engineer or hydrologist can be certain that Egypt is completely safe. The river has twice justified their uncertainty in the last twenty years, not least in most dramatic fashion within weeks of the diversion of the Nile in 1964 when it hazarded the very structure of the High Dam itself.[1]

Because there was no flood in the first forty years of this century to equal the worst excesses of the preceding forty, there began to be some complacency about the Nile defences. Sir Murdoch MacDonald put an end to this complacency in 1943 when he warned the country in a lecture in Cairo that the danger still existed, and his words were justified only three years later when the river again flowed over the frontiers in slow, high spate.

[1] See page 232.

'It was a terrifying sight, travelling along the Nile bank early in September, to see the river on one side nearing the top, whilst on the other the land was 10 or 12 feet below,' wrote an expert eye-witness[1]. The entire irrigation staff was mobilized under the Minister, Abdel Kawi Ahmed Pasha, who made his headquarters at the Mohammed Aly barrage and skilfully directed the defence like a military operation, moving men and materials swiftly to those points most threatened by the water.

Although the 1946 flood did not breach the banks, it reminded Egypt that the Nile was not yet tamed. It had compelled the irrigation engineers to take a calculated risk at Aswan by holding the crest of the flood. They were fortunately assisted at that time by flooding in the Sudan between Khartoum and Atbara, where the river overflowed its banks and covered many miles of low ground. This, by delaying the flood's arrival at Aswan, gave time to prepare against it, which is of supreme importance because there is always little time to spare; no estimate of the supply can be made until the rains have fallen in Ethiopia, and from the first warning given by the Roseires gauge seventy miles from the Sudan's distant frontier, the flood takes only ten days to reach Aswan and another five to Cairo.

The dam took the strain but if it had failed the disaster might have been incalculable. An area as big as Greater London was covered by the 1878 flood to a depth of two feet, and if so much water were now to break its bonds it could submerge the valley and the delta where almost 25 million people live.

The problem of Egypt has been apparent all this century. It needs more water to cultivate more land to feed its quickly increasing population, and the water of the Nile lost to the sea cannot be stored for the benefit of bad years. The Aswan Dam and its related works cannot with certainty save the country from disaster by flooding. One of the main reasons for the slowness of industrial development is the lack of sufficient power. Egypt is near the limit of Nile development along the traditional lines, and without a radical advance in method, it is destined to stay poor and over-populated.

The High Dam now being built at Aswan is the break-

[1] H. E. Hurst, *The Nile.*

through: the first advance on the system of Nile controls that the British inaugurated with the 1902 dam. Its fundamental purpose is to eliminate for ever Egypt's dependence on the annual flood by storing in the reservoir more water than is needed in any one year. This vision of security occupied the thoughts of British engineers before the turn of the century, when their lives and work on the Nile made them conscious of the perils of Egyptian agriculture and the shortcomings of the historic projects they were themselves executing. The High Dam germinated over sixty years from the seed of their anxiety.

CHAPTER TWO

The Forerunners and the Forgotten

The Nile has always reached out to the limits of human imagination. The ancient Egyptians made their gods in the image of the river. It came to them mysteriously from the arid emptiness of a world beyond their ken, tumbling at last through the rocks of the Aswan cataract to reach their fields, as sublime and as necessary as the rising and setting of the sun. It provoked in Winston Churchill a feeling of mystic reverence. For Emil Ludwig it was the most wonderful of all rivers, the image of man and his fate.

In the fifth century before Christ, Herodotus struggled up the river to Aswan only to see the river stretching away to the south and there was no one to tell him where it began its journey. Envoys of the Emperor Nero were compelled to turn back at the swamps of the Southern Sudan, and for 1,800 years – that is, until the middle of the last century – no one was able to get much farther. The map of Ptolemy, which showed the Nile stretching south from the Mediterranean Sea to two lakes hidden high 'in the Mountains of the Moon', was hardly challenged by a single fact in all that time. The unknown source was a fascination to geographers and to explorers; 'that impenetrable blank space in the centre of the continent', wrote Alan Moorehead, 'had become filled in imagination with a thousand monstrosities, dwarf men and cannibals with tails, animals as strange as the fabulous griffen and the salamander, huge inland seas, and mountains so high they defied all nature by bearing on their crests, in this equatorial heat, a mantle of perpetual snow'.[1]

It was not until the third quarter of last century that a succession of explorers penetrated this uncharted territory from the east and west coasts of the continent into a region which was indeed of great lakes and high mountains and there found the answer to the riddle of the river. Two decades of bickering, of nobility and suffering, of saintliness and sin, culminating in

[1] *The White Nile.*

Stanley's implacable journey to confirm Speke's discovery of the source of the Nile, brought them out of the forest, on to the high plateau, and face to face at last with Ptolemy's Mountains of the Moon. It was as though a window had thrown its light on one patch of darkest Africa.

Stanley's journey was in 1876. In the wake of the explorers came the missionary and the colonizer to open central Africa to settlers who made farms where there had been fables. Lower down the Nile its grandeur and challenge were not lost by man's knowledge of it. Other men, most of them drawn from the rivers of India, sailed boats on its placid waters in Egypt, rode donkeys and horses along its sultry banks, measured it and marked it with patience and skill, and from their prosaic diligence distilled new visions. 'When we consider the energies and labours of the men who achieved the great discoveries of the sources of the Nile,' wrote William Willcocks, 'it seems but a poor compensation to them to know that these sources can now be depicted on plans. It would be a triumph indeed and a real compensation if the resources of modern science could be employed to utilize these great lakes and, by the construction of suitable works, ensure a constant and plentiful supply of water to the Nile valley during the summer months when water is scarce and valuable as gold.'

After the silent centuries the time-lag was astonishingly short. Less than fifteen years after Stanley had established the source of the Nile, the imagination of Willcocks was converting the inland seas guarded by the Mountains of the Moon into domesticated reservoirs. He proposed to use them to store water, and then to clear a way for the White Nile through the swamps of the Southern Sudan; this, he said, with sublime simplicity, would accomplish all Egypt needed. He revealed an equally fine disregard for other difficulties: even as he was writing the Sudan was cut off from Egypt and the civilized world by dervish armies and only six years earlier General Gordon had been speared to death on the steps of his palace at Khartoum.

Mr Willcocks, noting in passing the military impediments and writing in prose that sometimes was lifted by inspiration above his prosaic engineering precision, described his visionary plan in Appendix III of his 1894 report to the Egyptian Government. But Britain's first task was to make Egypt solvent again. The administration wanted plans to prevent the Nile from washing away the farms of Egypt every few years, as it had done four times in the previous two decades, and to provide Nile water for two or three crops a year on as much of the land as possible. Mr Willcocks could dream dreams but his job was bread and butter. The Aswan Dam was the result.

Nevertheless, he saw from the outset that it was not enough to give Egypt year by year the water and security it required. The scheme of Nile control then, and since, was based on the measurement of the average flood, but Willcocks wrote in 1903 that the years of low supply should always be made the basis of calculation, 'for mean years are of no value since the surplus of one year is not available for the next'. Here, at the beginning of modern irrigation, was expressed the need for a reservoir to store water from year to year.

The Aswan Dam made no difference to the fact that in an abnormal year the rains from the African highlands could sweep away village after village in Egypt or be insufficient to fill the Aswan reservoir, which every year was emptied of its reserves to water the cotton and summer fallow land. 'Each year must stand on its own base,' wrote Willcocks, 'and there will never be any stable development of a tract of country depending on irrigation unless all the possibilities of drought and deficiency are put beyond the power of recurrence.' He and other British engineers persistently advocated the use of the equatorial lakes as storage reservoirs and regulators. 'There we can do with a sweep of a giant's hand more than can be done at all the remaining cataracts put together,' wrote Willcocks in 1901.[1] This idea of using the equatorial lakes survived more than half a century of study and dispute to become the first approved scheme for storing water beyond the needs of one year.

The Aswan Dam satisfied the needs of Egypt temporarily but most people assumed that it reached the limits of its growth when it was heightened for the second time. The relentless pressure of population, the country's insatiable demand for more water to give bigger and better harvests, the compelling desire for money to pay for schools, houses and hospitals, all these combined to

[1] Sir William Willcocks, *The Nile Reservoir Dam and After*. Preface to second edition.

force a fresh search for storage areas in the thirties of this century. The Second World War intervened; but in 1943, when the war had receded from Egypt, Sir Murdoch MacDonald told an audience at the Anglo-Egyptian Union in Cairo that the dam could easily be heightened a third time and this would enable it to hold any flood that came against it. No man was more qualified to speak, for he was the greatest living authority on the dam, with which he had been associated in one capacity or another from its inception. The Egyptian Government asked him for his plan and when he presented it the following year the Aswan site came back into the picture.

The need for more water and security was given fresh urgency by the threat, only narrowly escaped, of the high 1946 flood, and the Irrigation Department was asked to examine all possible methods of providing the necessary water *to extend Egyptian agriculture to the limit.* Dr H. E. Hurst, Mr R. B. Black and Yusef Simaika Bey, of the Department, were already well advanced in their monumental study of the Nile basin, and in Volume VII they presented a project for the entire Nile based on the storage capacity of the lakes. Dr Hurst, who has travelled the Nile from end to end more than once in his sixty years' association with it and is the greatest living authority on its hydrology, spent twelve years assessing the storage capacity required to give Egypt all the water it needs every year, irrespective of the variations in the annual river supply.

Egypt requires about 63 milliards (that is, 63 thousand millions) of cubic yards of water a year. In extreme years, such as 1878–9, there can be an excess of 130 milliards that waste themselves in the sea, but there are years when there is no surplus at all or even not enough, as in 1913–14 when the total supply to Egypt was only 54 milliards. Even within any one year the Nile can be fickle. During the critical period from February to July, when Egypt needs about 29 milliards, the supply can vary from 47 milliards (in 1879) to 9 milliards (in 1914).

Dr Hurst set himself the task of making mathematical sense of the Nile's incalculability and has himself described his work.[1]

> 'There were obviously two lines of approach' [he wrote]. 'One was the experimental and statistical one of collecting

[1] *The Nile.*

the discharges of a number of rivers and calculating the storage capacity to equalize the discharge in each case. The other was the mathematical approach through the theory of probability assuming that the variability of the discharge of a river is similar to the variability of chance events. The first method led to an enormous amount of computation, since to deal statistically with a question one must have a mass of material. For this purpose records extending over many years were required, and these are not numerous in the domain of rivers, so work was extended to rainfall statistics, which appeared to be similar in their characteristics. Then followed the inclusion of temperatures and barometric pressures. The common characteristics of all these is that they have similar frequency distributions. The idea of a frequency distribution is a simple one, with wide applications to many subjects, including biology, social science and engineering. . . . The use of temperatures or any other statistics merely means that we go through the same arithmetical process as we should if they represented quantities of water, and we arrive at a figure which, in the case of water, would be required storage capacity. That is, we are using a property common to similar sets of numbers – a usual practice for mathematicians and physicists. The longest series of river or rainfall records, excluding those of the Roda Nileometer, do not reach 200 years, and the same is true of temperature and pressures. In order to get a longer series of figures, it was necessary to make use of the work of Dr A. E. Douglass in measuring the rings of giant trees of America, and also of measurements made by Baron de Greer, of the thickness of varves. These are the annual layers of mud deposited on ancient lake beds. The tree rings extend to nearly 1,000 years and the varves in some cases to 4,000 years. In all, seventy-five different phenomena were analysed and 690 computations made of storage capacity.'

Not content with records of varves that were the contemporaries of the Great Pyramid, Dr Hurst proceeded to work on the 'variable factors' – the element of chance – needed to take account of successive good or bad years, for he had by this time acquired a healthy respect for the Nile's ability to disregard the law of averages: '. . . there is no such thing in many natural phenomena as a true mean . . .', he, and his colleague, Dr R. P. Black, note in this connection.[1] Dr Hurst found himself at last verifying his formula for the standard variation of chance events 'by tossing a set of coins 1,000 times, by cutting cards 1,000 times from a special pack . . . and by using a set of 1,000 random numbers made up from the published numbers of bonds drawn for redemption'.

If the behaviour of the eminent hydrologist seemed bizarre to any onlooker, it had its part in Egypt ultimately staking its shirt, more confidently than punters usually do, on a calculated chance. When he and Dr Black were asked in 1955 to investigate the means of making the maximum amount of water available to Egypt and the Sudan, they reported in favour of the High Dam. The mathematical work, however, had not the dam in mind at the time. They were seeking the scientific starting-point for any scheme of Nile control, and came to the conclusion that it should be based on nothing less than a century of floods. Hurst, Black and Simaika thus created the idea of 'century storage'. They then went back, broadly speaking, to the nineteenth-century scheme for using Lakes Victoria, Albert and Tana, and cutting a canal through the Sudd, the swamps of the Southern Sudan, in which half the flow of the White Nile is lost. They advocated the use of Lake Victoria as the main reservoir with Lake Albert as a small reservoir and regulator, and they hoped also to use Lake Tana, in Ethiopia, for storage. Associated with the use of the lakes and the cutting of the swamps was a complete series of proposals for works on the Nile in the Sudan and Egypt.

The countries concerned, mainly Britain and Egypt, reached agreement on the overall scheme and it was estimated that twenty years would be needed to complete the works. Many people believe that the scheme is still the best possible way of conserving and controlling the Nile. The Owen Falls Dam was in due course built a mile and a half below the exit of the river from Lake Victoria, which became as a result the biggest reservoir in the world, and a source of hydro-electric power for Uganda.

[1] Report on Hydrological Investigations on how the Maximum Volume of the Nile Water may be made available for development in Egypt and the Sudan – Dr H. E. Hurst and Mr R. P. Black.

Even as century storage was under consideration, a Greek agronomist, Mr Adrian Daninos, produced an entirely new project for Aswan. There was at the time a dispute raging among experts on the design and wisdom of building a hydro-electric station at the existing dam, that veteran of the Nile whose benefactions were not yet at their limit. Daninos proposed in 1947 that the hydro-electric station should be built at a new dam, which, he suggested, should be constructed four miles to the south of it. His scheme made little impact, and the Egyptian Government proceeded to adopt the century storage programme as its official policy in 1948.

Adrian Daninos is an Egyptian citizen born of Greek parents at Alexandria in 1887 and he is still living, if somewhat obscurely, in an apartment in central Cairo whence his still fertile brain pursues and publicizes a plan for a new kind of agricultural community which, he contends, can save the world from hunger. (He wants Reading University in England to establish a pilot project to prove its workability.) His father was Daninos Pasha, who was associated with the khedivial court and excavated the Meidum statues of Princess Nafrit and Prince Ra-Hatpu of the Third Dynasty. Adrian was trained as an agricultural engineer at the School of Agriculture at Giza, just outside Cairo, and then qualified as a lawyer in Paris. He married a Welsh girl, Miss Williams. Throughout his long life he has been a visionary, particularly concerned with development of the Nile in Egypt and as long ago as 1912, in association with the Hon. Walter Trefusis, he proposed that a hydro-electric station should be built at the then brand-new Aswan Dam. He claims – and there do not appear to be records of any earlier plan – to be the originator of the whole concept of Egyptian industrialization by hydro-electric power. The 1912 proposal incorporated a plan to build a nitrogen fertilizer plant at Aswan, and as his scheme evolved through the years, it included in the thirties land reclamation, irrigation and river navigation, and in the forties the production of steel from indigenous ore by electric power. He advocated that the new land brought into cultivation should be distributed among landless peasants and that the fertilizer should be shared on a co-operative system among the small farmers. Except for the navigation scheme, the Daninos vision of development is very much the development as it has taken or is taking place.

In 1922 he advocated the then revolutionary idea that the fertilizer plant should be a nationalized undertaking and that cheap credit should be provided for small farmers and peasants. The credit facilities were provided soon afterwards and when, nearly forty years later, the Aswan hydro-electric station began functioning, the first claim on its output was the new nitrogen fertilizer factory. The industrial development of Egypt as a whole including the manufacture of steel, is to be powered by electricity from Aswan, and the new land will be shared among peasants and the fertilizer distributed on credit through co-operatives.

It is beyond question that Daninos conceived the High Dam scheme. In proposing in 1912 the hydro-electrification of Aswan – without which the dam could hardly be built at all – he first formulated the line of development that led him nearly forty years later to the idea and the Government eventually to its construction.

In 1912 Daninos and Trefusis asked for a concession to utilize hydro-electric power at Aswan to reclaim 1·5 million acres of state land over fifteen years at the rate of 100,000 a year. The whole enterprise, including the construction of the works, was estimated to cost £E30 million, which they undertook to find themselves if the Government would repay the sum at 5 per cent interest over thirty years. Sir William Garstin expressed interest in the scheme in a letter to Daninos, but Sir Murdoch Macdonald and other experts condemned it as impracticable. Daninos sought advice from G. Tofani, the technical adviser to Siemens, and Engineer Ratti, a turbine specialist, and then addressed himself directly to Lord Kitchener, and he contends that he obtained from him the assurance that he and his associate would either be given the concession for the project or charge of its execution on behalf of the Government. On the basis of these 'acquired rights', Daninos and Trefusis sued the Egyptian Government a quarter of a century later.

The outbreak of the First World War prevented further consideration of the scheme by Lord Kitchener, but hostilities had no sooner finished than Daninos and Trefusis returned to the attack with a new and detailed study. In 1920, the Egyptian Government invited them to enter into a public competition for the right to execute the project and, while reserving their 'acquired rights', they did so. Seven days before adjudication, the Government withdrew the scheme. In the succeeding decades, the Government did not acknowledge any rights on the part of Daninos and his partner, and doubtless the evolution of hydroelectric techniques left little that was exclusively theirs beyond the idea. In 1932 the Government again called for the public adjudication of plans and again cancelled it, and in 1936 the Minister of Finance announced that the Government had decided that two firms, chosen without adjudication, would execute the project. Daninos maintained his vigorous protests to Ministers and presented his scheme to a Board of International Consultants who were called in to advise. Before this preliminary stage was past, the Second World War began.

In May 1945, Daninos resumed his campaign with a note on 'the total exploitation of Egypt's resources', in which he contended that the cultivated acreage could be 13 million acres – a contention no one has supported since – and advocated the elimination of all open drains, which deprived Egypt of about 10 per cent of its cultivated area, and the building of a steel works. The Government, however, put to adjudication a plan prepared by Abdel Aziz Ahmed and Messrs. Kennedy and Donkin, the British firm. Daninos and Trefusis promptly took their case against the Government to the Mixed Courts, but by the time the case came to court in November 1947, Trefusis was dead and his son, Schomberg Charles Trefusis and Harold Hamilton Williams, a British engineer who was Daninos's nephew, appeared as concessionaires of his estate. In demanding their 'acquired rights', the plaintiffs asked for the suspension of adjudication on the Ahmed-Donkin scheme, which, as it happened, was progressively postponed without the court's intervention.

While his case was in preparation, Daninos spent several months touring barrages and hydro-electric projects in Europe and the United States, in the course of which he told the world's Press through the news agencies that the Egyptian Government was jeopardizing the country's future. When he returned to

Cairo in April 1947 he was not received by the international consultants, who were advising on the Ahmed-Donkin plan, until the day before they left, but he then discovered that they had never heard of his scheme. His persistence in his claims, his criticism of Government plans, his pursuit of everyone in authority from the Prime Minister down, and his court case, had doubtless made him a confounded nuisance, even a crank, in the eyes of the Government.

It was at this stage, nevertheless, that he put forward the plan for a new barrage at Aswan to impound 13 milliard cubic yards of water, and a lock to permit navigation by ships up to 2,000 tons, all to be completed in three years at a cost of £E12 million; the construction of a hydro-electric station of 125,000 kw, to be executed in three stages at a total cost of £E15 million; the construction of a fertilizer plant to produce 600,000 tons of fertilizer a year at a cost of £E6 million and of a steel works to produce 100,000 tons of steel a year at a cost of £E2 million; and the laying of power lines to the deltas and elsewhere. He persuaded a consortium of British firms to submit an offer to execute the works.

This was not the High Dam scheme. This was the time of the dispute among experts as to the wisdom of building a hydro-electric station at the old dam which, some said, would be damaged by the vibrations caused by the powerful turbines and it must have seemed that Daninos was exploiting the dispute to revive his own proposals. Mahmoud Fahmy el-Nokrashy Pasha, the Prime Minister, agreed that a representative of the consortium should come to Cairo, but when the representative arrived he was not received and the international consultants said they were not charged to consider the consortium project.

Still undeterred, Daninos, who had Williams collaborating, entered into an agreement with Luigi Gallioli, an Italian engineer who was proprietor of Studio Tecnice Ingegnore Gallioli (S.T.I.G.) to prepare a definitive project in opposition to the Government scheme. Daninos had himself come to the conclusion that there were possibilities of water storage behind Aswan greatly in excess of anything formerly considered and he took Gallioli to Aswan to examine his theory. They returned from Aswan to advocate the Daninos–Gallioli project, claiming that they had established the possibility of constructing a barrage at Aswan capable of holding easily the entire flood of the Nile at normal times to a total of 186 milliards of cubic yards, with a constant flow capable of generating 16 milliards of kilowatt hours a year. On January 12, 1948, at the first meeting of the year of L'Institut d'Egypte, a highly reputable organization which Napoleon had started, Daninos presented a paper on 'the total use of the waters of the Nile basin'.[1] In this paper he announced that it was possible to build at Aswan the greatest reservoir in the world: four times greater than the Boulder Dam, which had itself a capacity of 52 milliards of cubic yards. 'The new fact,' he added, 'is the sensational discovery that we had made in the Aswan region, of the existence of an immense natural basin capable of retaining, by the construction of a single barrage, the flood waters of two consecutive years.'

Here was the High Dam scheme. The estimate of the capacity of the reservoir at 186 milliards, although 40 milliards more than the intended reservoir, is a capacity that could have been attained if it had been necessary and the funds were available. Daninos presented to the Institute the arguments which have since been used by the revolutionary Government: that for the first time his proposals envisaged works that could be executed entirely in Egypt and under Egypt's full sovereignty; one could, he said, commence work on it 'tomorrow', whereas the scheme for developing the Nile as a whole would require international agreements and the solution of many other difficulties. On an estimated capacity of 186 milliards, he estimated the annual discharge at 110 milliards, the storage of all flood waters, full protection against flooding, the regulation of the discharge throughout the year, and the provision of more hydro-electric power than was possible through any other scheme. By including the reclamation of 200,000 acres at Wadi Rayan and 2,750,000 acres in the Qattara depression, Daninos estimated that over 5 million acres could be brought into cultivation and another 1 million converted from basin to perennial irrigation. According to his calculations at the time, the barrage could be built for £E40 millions and the hydro-electric plant for £E30 millions.

[1] 'L'utilisation intégral des eaux du bassin du Nil', *Bulletin de L'Institut d'Egypte*, T.XXX – Session 1947–48.

The surprising thing about Daninos's proposal was not that some of his figures proved inaccurate but that, on such scanty opportunities for survey, he was able to achieve reasonable accuracy. Hundreds of thousands of pounds were eventually to be spent on surveys for the High Dam project and in the end it was broadly as Daninos presented it. His proposal that a lock should be provided for ships over 2,000 tons was, however, not included in the final scheme (and Daninos remains to this day a severe critic of the omission). Curiously, since he had argued a quarter of a century earlier that a fertilizer plant at Aswan would be uneconomic without electricity, he did not foresee that it would be almost impossible to build the new dam unless the hydro-electric power of the old were available, for it was part of his idea that the station at his new barrage would replace the Ahmed–Donkin plan.

After further studies with Williams and Gallioli, Daninos formulated his plan in greater detail, renaming it the Daninos 1949 Project, and made it over to an International Nile Valley Syndicate, which he had formed in 1948 without any Egyptian members. He secured the co-operation of Professor J. Aubert of France, Professor C. M. White of England and Professor G. de Marchi of Italy, as international consultants. Mr R. B. Black, associate of Hurst and Simaika, wrote in a letter to Daninos in May 1950 that he 'had made out a good case for a survey to determine whether the capacity exists in the valley south of Aswan to enable the whole volume of the river to be dealt with on the principle of century storage'. Dr Hurst, who was completing his book *The Nile* when the details came into his possession, wrote in the book: 'If this idea could be realized it would provide a simple solution to many complicated problems and avoid some political difficulties. But, as is always the case, in avoiding some difficulties it encounters others. The pamphlet is rather like the prospectus of a company in which the claims are somewhat exaggerated and the difficulties passed over. It is a very long way from this stage to the presentation of the final project, in which pros and cons have been duly weighed and detailed plans can be prepared for construction.' Hurst nevertheless concluded that the scheme was 'worthy of some examination to see whether the difficulties are as formidable as they first appear'. In 1951, John

Lucien Savage, one of the most distinguished civil engineers of the United States, who had been consultant on many great plans all over the world, including the T.V.A. project in his own country, wrote to Daninos undertaking 'to act as your personal consultant'. He agreed to visit Aswan on the return leg of a world tour that he was about to undertake.

Daninos went back to Europe in 1951 and in a Press conference on March 30, as reported by Reuters, he stated that his international experts had confirmed that a huge reservoir could be created behind the new dam in Egypt. While they recognized the value of the scheme for developing the Nile as a whole, they thought his scheme was an inescapable complement and, because of the immediate results it would achieve, deserved priority. He further stated that an international syndicate of industrial firms was ready to make a comprehensive offer for the entire project from the building of the dam and the power station to the reclaiming of the new lands and the execution of associated industrial projects. Later, on his return to Egypt, he came round to the idea of associating an Egyptian company which he proposed to form with Mohammed Taher Pasha, a descendant of the royal family and President of the Royal Agricultural Society, as its chairman. He also appealed to the United Nations, the International Bank and Point Four for technical and financial assistance.

Although Daninos was, as usual, in touch with the Prime Minister and Finance Minister, the Government showed no interest in the Daninos scheme and it could make no progress without their full support. The international experts gave their opinion on his data, but their support was at this stage tantamount only to agreement that a prima facie case had been made out, as Dr Black also suggested, for a thorough study of the project; the international consortium could only have agreed to consider the undertaking to build it; and international organizations neither could nor would give aid on the suggestion of an individual.

In any case, it was a highly disturbed period in Egypt: the Daninos proposals coincided with the Palestine war; Mahmoud el-Nokrashy Pasha was assassinated in 1948; in 1951 the Wafd Government launched a guerrilla war against the British in the canal zone; in 1952 Cairo was burnt by the mob and the Wafd Government fell. Egypt was tumbling about the ears of its rulers and the moment of dissolution left no heart for the passionate act of creating the greatest living monument in Egypt's long history and one of the greatest in the history of the world. Once again disastrous events stood between Daninos and any prospect he might have had for Government adoption of his dream: to the world at large, and even to the majority of the Egyptians themselves, his idea for transforming the whole future of the country passed unnoticed. Yet there were some engineers whose imagination had been fired by it, and when the Government of young officers had time to collect their wits in the first months of power, it was the Daninos scheme which was brought to their attention.

But by this time there was no place whatever for the old man of the river, Adrian Daninos. He now bustles about Cairo in pursuit of his scheme of new agricultural communities to save the world from hunger but, at long last, he has abandoned his plans for the Nile to others, seeking instead the opportunity to establish his communal system on a large stretch of land on the western seaboard of Egypt. At a mention of the High Dam, his mind will leap alertly to a critique of its present execution, notably over the omission of the lock for navigation, but he talks as an onlooker whose part in it has no more than a place in history. 'At 72,' he remarks, 'I have no need either for ambition or money.'

CHAPTER THREE

Decision and Conflict

The creative impulse was absent from Egypt in 1952. A brooding pessimism lay heavy on the land, and the people, weary of the palace and the pasha, were cynical and despairing. The patriotic fervour of the crusade against the British in the previous autumn had subsided in squalid political manœuvring between politicians and the King. The pitiful deaths of some brave auxiliary policemen who had mistaken the politicians' charade for a national war set the fuse to popular protest in January and Cairo was burnt by its inhabitants in a fit of anger. When the capital emerged from the flames, the leaders still tinkered with the task. They promised a new deal, a purge of incompetents, the punishment of the corrupt; they restored the old order, purged very few and punished none. When the Government fell in the summer it proved extremely difficult to replace it. Even the politicians were sick of themselves.

A deep fatalism about the country's future was the unspoken cause of common discontent. Every thinking Egyptian knew of the insidious advance of poverty over the last half-century and that little was being done about it. The country was steadily eating itself to death and no one appeared to have a plan or combination of plans to save it.

Such hope as remained was focused on the army. When the fires burnt themselves out in January and Cairo lay sullenly silent, the truth that it alone sustained the power of the State was revealed. Soon a rumour spread abroad, which neither repression nor censorship could silence, that the army was on the side of the people. Trusted Pressmen heard of a movement of Free Officers which had its own intelligence service from which they could learn many secrets, and the newspapers were full of obscure hints for those who could read between the lines. The King knew of the plot against him, and, as he could not use the army against itself, formed his own secret officers' movement, pledged to destroy his enemies.

He failed, and the Free Officers seized power on July 23. The State, for long rotten to the core, had crumbled without resistance to the first stroke against it, and three days later King Farouk and his family sailed away from Alexandria into well-deserved exile. The Egyptian revolution had begun.

The people were delighted by these events, although nothing had positively changed for the better and the new leaders were unknown. Those who paused to think on the morning of the *coup* wondered what a few inexperienced officers would do about problems that had defied the wisdom of more than a century of modern Egypt. The Free Officers, however, were not in doubt, and they committed themselves to the opinion that the living standards could and would be raised. This promise was born out of ignorance of the facts through faith in the doctrines of Egyptian nationalism, according to which common people could be lifted from the age-long rut of poverty by a combination of industrial development and agrarian reform.

This was correctly termed an 'aspiration', for there was no coherent policy, much less a programme, to achieve it, and the leaders were held together by little more than a pervasive radicalism. They were a heterogeneous collection of theorists and idealists, passionately committed to their purpose but utterly confused about how to attain it, with the traditionalists who looked to the fanatical Moslem Brotherhood for a state ruled according to the Koran on one wing, on the other the pro-communist elements who, pursing the 'modernist' trend in nationalism to its limit, wanted to smash the stultifying social shell of Islam and create a secular, socialist state, and, in between, the hard core of pragmatists who wanted machines more than ideologies. Colonel Abdel Nasser, the first among nominal equals in the executive of the Free Officers, belonged to the centre.

Their first act was to decree the agrarian reform which limited ownership to 200 acres. This plan for land reform was supported by all nationalists, but whatever benefits it could bring to some Egyptians, it would not necessarily enrich the country as a whole. Egypt needed more water for the cultivation of more land, more power to drive more machines, more machines to be driven, and more materials to feed the machines, and it needed them all together and as quickly as possible. Had they not heard of a project gigantic enough to match all these requirements? Undeterred by lack of cash or political credit, they tore apart the dusty pigeon-holes of the ministries in search of the answer to their country's problem which, they were convinced, had been left there to rot by traitors and saboteurs, and they emerged almost at once with the High Dam scheme. It was so ambitious in dimensions, in engineering techniques, and in cost, that the swiftness to embark upon it implied more faith than study, but the officers were young enough to hope when most of their elders had ceased even to pray. It meant the spending of about $1,120 million to lay the biggest dam in the world across the Nile, on a bed of sand and sludge nearly 300 feet deep, the construction of the world's biggest hydro-electric station deep in solid granite, and the extensive development of desert and farmland.

A sceptical world said it never could or would be built. At the time it seemed no more than the impertinent ambition of a Government which, internationally speaking, was still wet behind the ears, still on the verge of bankruptcy, and led by colonels and majors who were reckoned by some people to be no better than second-rate staff captains. What other reason than conceit and egotism could explain the desire to build a dam in one of the hottest and most arid regions in the world when the century storage programme already approved and planned was a better way of controlling the Nile from its source to the sea? Later, when Nasser declared that nothing would be allowed to stand in the way of the High Dam, it became known as his 'pyramid', as his mad ambition to out-pharaoh the pharaohs with a structure to equal all the pyramids put together. The heady phrases with which he decorated his descriptions of the plan gave colour to such opinions; and, in truth, it would have been strange if any man within whose power it lay to command so vast and wonderful an enterprise had not been carried away by the very thought of it. The desire to leave behind this immortal monument to their work for Egypt unquestionably moved Nasser and his men to the supreme effort to achieve it.

Yet, in the final count, it was the harsh fact of the nation's poverty that spurred ambition, and there were others less starry-eyed than the officers who believed the High Dam must be built. Dr Abdel Gelil el-Emery, the hard-headed Finance Minister who steered the revolutionary Government clear of bankruptcy before he fell from grace, said that the High Dam was essential to Egypt and that there would be no place for the big cars and refrigerators of America, the fashionable silks and satins of Paris and Rome and the wools and worsteds of London – those luxuries cramming the shops of Cairo – once Egypt set about building it. As under-secretary at the ministry before the revolution he had witnessed the waste of wealth abroad, the frittering away of millions of sterling and of other currencies, and he recognized that the rich of Egypt would, in one way or another, be compelled to pay for the dam. 'It will herald an era of unheard austerity for them, but the mass of the people may even be better off by the wages they earn working on it', Dr Abdel Gelil said.[1]

The Free Officers decided to pursue the High Dam scheme within two months of coming to power. Their minds leaped across the years of its construction to the day when it would offer a dazzlingly simple solution to the age-old problems of Egypt, the break-through, the first great step forward into the progressive future they had promised the people. (When *The Economist* published in 1960 Professor Walt Whitman Rostow's theory that sufficient capital investment could bring a country to the point of economic take-off from which it could advance beyond the stage of persistent underdevelopment, it was seized on in Egypt as the expression of what the Government was trying to do.) Not that the dam itself could raise Egypt from rags to riches, for the increase in population during the decade spent in building it would be sufficient to consume the products of the new land brought into cultivation. Its importance lay in the fact that it would 'buy' time for development because during the ten years of construction, for the first time since the first decade of this century, Egypt would at least not get poorer in terms of agricultural production. Further, the dam would provide the power for an industrial programme which, taking place side by side with agricultural expansion, would raise the standard of

[1] Speaking to the author.

living. Every other development would then be clear profit over population. In short, it seemed to the Free Officers that the High Dam would make the impossible possible.

They rejected, at least for the time being, the storage scheme based on the African lakes. Although they conceded that in a perfectly ordered world the lake scheme might be good for Egypt, they concluded that in practice it depended too much on co-ordination of many national interests and priorities. More than half the twenty-year period had passed before the first of the Nile development projects was completed at the Owen Falls. Egypt could not afford to see the years – each of which meant an extra half-million people to feed – drift by, when she could herself control a plan to build the High Dam within a specified period.

The dam would also give the Egyptian a sense of security he had never known. His utter dependence on the flow of water from the African highlands makes him sensitive to the danger of any interference with the river. Sir William Willcocks had emphasized this danger at the end of the last century when he pointed out that the complete blocking of Lake Victoria would raise the level of the lake only 20 inches a year, which made it easy to deprive Egypt of summer water for ten or fifteen years in succession. Lake Victoria was, he wrote, the key of the Nile, 'and whoever holds it has the destinies of Egypt in the hollow of his hand'. Sir William himself figured in a famous libel action in Cairo over his unjustified allegation that Sir Murdoch MacDonald had falsified the records of the Nile in order to justify the development of cotton cultivation in the Sudan at the expense of Egypt's water supply; and the trial was itself the culmination of four years of intense suspicion among Egyptians that Britain was preparing to sacrifice their country for the sake of the Sudan. One could argue in this day and age that the world would not sit back while Egypt was starved to death; but the Free Officers contended that countries did not usually rest their vital security on the presumption of international virtue. (They were to justify their attitude in 1956 when a British Member of Parliament proposed in the Commons that President Nasser should be compelled to capitulate over the nationalization of the Suez Canal Company by a diversion of the Nile near its source). As they saw it, the dam would eliminate any danger because its reservoir could keep the country supplied with water until world opinion compelled the offenders to restore the Nile.

Having decided to build the dam, the Officers urgently needed outside help on the design, and at this crucial moment, the Palestine problem, which in 1947 had distracted attention from the Daninos proposals, came to their aid. The West German Government had agreed in September to pay Israel and representatives of world Jewry 3,000 million marks as compensation for Jewish sufferings under Hitler, and when the Arab states bitterly criticized the agreement on the grounds that it strengthened their enemy, undertook to equalize the aid to Israel by preparing the High Dam project. The Hochtief and Dortmund Union was given the task by the German Government.[1] On October 18, less than three months after the *coup d'état*, the union submitted proposals for the preparation of tenders for the design, execution and financing of the dam. Without wasting time, on November 22, the Egyptian Government invited the two firms to send technical experts to Aswan to draft the designs.

This preparatory work occupied two years, during which the Hochtief and Dortmund Union in fact prepared two plans. In November 1954 a Board of International Consultants approved the second, or supplementary, design, commenting that such a dam would be 'as safe as the safest among existing earth and rock-fill dams resting on sediments'. The urgent need was now for money, of which there was an acute shortage. The current account in sterling, on which Egypt relied for its overseas buying, was almost empty, and more than £400 million once held in London as credit from the war years had almost all been wasted by the former ruling class on foreign luxuries and holidays abroad. Clearly the Government could not build the dam without foreign help.

[1] The Hochtief and Dortmund Union was an association of two firms, Messrs. Hochtief Aktiengesellschaft, Essen, and Rheinstahl-Union-Bruckenbau Aktiengesellschaft, Dortmund. They formed a consortium. J. M. Voith, Maschinenfabrik, Heidenheim, turbine specialists, SSW-Siemens-Schuckert-Werke, Erlangen and A.E.G.-Allgemeine Electricitatsgesellschaft, and MAN-Maschinenfabrik, Mainz-Gustatsburg, specialists with Rheinstahl-Union-Bruckenbau for hydraulic steel structures. The consortium worked under the direction of Hochtief.

Aid on the scale required by the High Dam depended on foreign confidence and this was not over-abundant. At the outset of the revolution the powers naturally regarded with caution the unknown and self-appointed arbiters of Egypt's destiny who, until that moment, had been no more than a mutinous group in the army. The King and the pashas had been poor in the world's respect, but those who replaced them talked constantly of revolution and it could well be that behind their façade of respectable intentions they had much more dangerous policies in mind. Revolutionary régimes, in any case, were often unstable.

Events in the first two years suggested that the Egyptian Government was no exception. Nasser emerged as the true leader early in the day but his leadership was challenged by the extreme wings of his own movement, first by the communist fringe and then by the Moslem brotherhood. The left-wing revolt was defeated with relative ease but the challenge of the brotherhood was much more serious and sustained. The movement had two million members, powerful wings in some other Arab countries and highly organized terrorist cells some of which contained seasoned assassins. The leaders, believing they were the real generators of the revolution, demanded a virtual veto over the Government's decisions, and when Nasser refused it they instigated opposition of increasing intensity and violence. This culminated in the summer of 1954 in riots in which nine people were killed and thirty-five wounded.

Nasser had no illusions about the brotherhood's inclination to violence and was fully aware that they had ample stocks of arms and explosives. Nevertheless, he fought back, knowing that in doing so he had either to destroy the movement or be murdered by it. An attempt to assassinate him was duly made on October 26 in Alexandria. Its failure spelt doom to the brotherhood. Most of its leaders were in prison before dawn, hundreds of its members joined them before the week was out, and 4,000 were rounded up before the end of the purge.

The defeat of the brotherhood also completed the elimination from the Government of General Neguib, its president and nominal leader. Chosen as their instrument by the Free Officers because of his valour in the Palestine war, his devotion to the army and his contempt for the King, Neguib was nevertheless by nature conservative, and more and more as time passed he had grown to dislike the policies of the young officers around him. The people loved him for his ready smile, his rugged appearance, his pipe-smoking calm, his readiness to listen to complaints and his lack of fanaticism, and he had come at last to believe that the revolution existed in the cheering multitude, that without his popular leadership there could be no revolution. This attitude had made him a ready tool in the hands of the opposition, and he had been used in turn by the communists, the remnants of the old régime and finally the brotherhood. When his equivocal connections with the brotherhood leaders became known after the attempted assassination he was put under house arrest at Marg, a few miles outside Cairo, and disappeared from public view.

His elimination brought to a successful conclusion Nasser's initial struggle for power almost at the precise moment that the international consultants gave their decision on the High Dam. Whether there would be foreign aid for the dam therefore depended to a great extent on the assessment of Nasser, who some people thought to be a communist and a dangerous fanatic. On the whole, however, the tide of opinion was flowing in his favour. His skilful victory over the extremists enhanced his reputation at home and abroad and his persecution of the communists after their defeat did much to reassure the cautious Western powers. Above all, his conduct of the dispute with Britain over the canal zone base in 1954 was evidence of an encouraging statesmanship.

This dispute was the keystone of international confidence, for it was self-evident that Britain and her friends were unlikely to give aid as long as the prospect of armed conflict over the zone existed. As late as 1953, Nasser himself had threatened to 'pull down the temple' about his head if the British did not evacuate the zone and the extremists all along advocated the use of force. In 1954, however, Nasser revived the faltering negotiations with Britain and in the face of virulent opposition from the brotherhood, who made his new policy the excuse for the attempt on his life, he pushed them through to a successful conclusion in October. Therefore when the High Dam design was approved in November he was in a better position to ask for aid than anyone else. The fate of the High Dam had, indeed, been at stake throughout his struggle for power, for none of his opponents could or would have fostered the international confidence needed to finance it.

Nasser himself was confident enough. The season was just beginning in upper Egypt and dragomen conducting tourists up the Nile pointed to an emphatic white line drawn vertically on each bank of the river at the Aswan cataract, remarking that a mountain of a dam would soon be built there. Nasser had ordered the painting of these lines so that popular imagination could etch in the greatness he now thought certain to come.

Britain, the United States, France and West Germany, which had all followed the design stage with close interest, certainly had the matter of aid in mind, and the World Bank sent experts to judge whether the dam would offer Egypt economic benefits commensurate with the substantial credits likely to be required. The bank's final report was not ready until February 1956 but the interim opinions were encouraging enough for an international consortium to be formed in September 1955 for the purpose of building the dam.[1] Britain and the United States informed the Egyptian Government in November that they would offer loans for the first stage of the work if the bank's final report proved favourable.

When this report was delivered it declared the dam to be technically sound as conceived and that it 'would be the dominating feature of Egyptian economic development over the next decade'. The Bank, the United States Government and the British Government thereupon submitted *aides mémoires* in which the Bank offered to advance $200 million, the United States $55 million and Britain $15 million. All the loans were intended for the first stage of the dam's construction and were interdependent. The Hochtief and Dortmund Union and the French

[1] The consortium consisted of the group of West German firms brought together in the Hochtief and Dortmund Union; George Wimpey & Co., Ltd, the British Electric Co., and British Insulated Callendars Cables Ltd, all of Britain and the French firms, Grands Travaux de Marseille, Sociétiés Françaises de Dragages et de Travaux Publiques, Société des Forges et Ateliers Creusot, and the Société Général de Constructions Electriques et Méchaniques Alsthome. Other smaller firms were also associated.

firms in the consortium continued to negotiate with their own Governments for additional financial aid.

Mr Eugene Black, President of the World Bank, reported 'substantial agreement' after a meeting with President Nasser in Cairo on February 9 and for a moment it seemed as though the financial hurdle had been surmounted. At this critical stage President Nasser hesitated. Fearing that the Anglo-American offer had been limited to the first stage of construction so that political pressure could be imposed on him by threats to refuse money for later work, he submitted amendments to the *aides mémoires* which, in effect asked the two powers to commit themselves to completion of the dam. This they refused to do, and all through the spring of 1956 Nasser neither accepted nor rejected the proffered aid.

This check to the financial arrangements was due to the sharp decline in confidence between the two Western powers and Egypt during 1955. The co-operation expected to grow from the Anglo–Egyptian agreement of 1954 never materialized and the year was barely out before it became clear that Nasser's Middle Eastern policy was in conflict with British interests and Britain thought he should mind his own Egyptian business.

The immediate cause of dispute was the idea of 'perimeter defence' – the alliance of four 'northern tier' countries, Turkey, Iraq, Iran and Pakistan – which the United States and Britain encouraged. It existed in embryo in an alliance of Turkey and Pakistan even before the Anglo–Egyptian agreement and Nasser's bitter opposition to Iraq's association with it was well known. He hoped that the agreement would set a pattern for relations between Iraq and Britain that would keep Iraq out of the proposed pact, but in January 1955 Iraq joined with Turkey in what became known as the Baghdad Pact and was the nucleus of the 'northern tier' system.[1]

Nasser correctly concluded that one purpose of Britain and the United States was to limit his influence in the region. He decided that the arms he wanted for defence against Israel would now go to Iraq for the improbable purpose of fighting Russia

[1] Pakistan, Iran and Britain joined the pact and the United States became 'associated' with it.

and that the Arab Collective Security Pact, which he desired to make the instrument of regional defence, would stay moribund for lack of help. He launched a successful campaign in the Arab world against the Iraqi Government in the course of which his renewed distrust of Britain was manifest.

Israel was quick to exploit the rift. Her uneasy frontiers with Egypt and the Egyptian-controlled Gaza strip had been quiet for some time when on February 28 she launched a regular force against Egyptian military headquarters in Gaza, wiping out the defenders and a truck-load of reinforcements that advanced to the relief. This attack gave urgency to the Egyptian demand for arms which had first been submitted in 1952 and Nasser now warned that he would go to Russia if the arms were not forthcoming. Both Britain and the United States regarded this warning as bluff, but after two more Israeli attacks, Britain delivered a small quantity of first-class arms, including some Gladiator tanks, which had been ordered and paid for by the pre-revolutionary Government in 1950. They were not enough for Nasser's needs and in September he shocked the Western powers by announcing the Czech arms deal, which he negotiated through Russia.

Nasser's relations with the Soviet *bloc* had been steadily improving for some time. He had negotiated an oil deal with Russia in 1954 and the proportion of Egyptian cotton bought by the *bloc* was increasing. Chou En-lai agreed at the Bandung Conference in May 1955 to buy $28 million worth. The Western powers were disturbed by this trend but regarded the arms deal as a much graver matter, opening a new phase of Soviet collaboration and influence in the region.

The arms deal occurred at a time when Britain and the United States were already aware that the World Bank experts were going to report in favour of the High Dam, and they had therefore to decide whether in these new circumstances they were ready to help. In neither country was the climate of opinion in favour of doing so, for Nasser was widely regarded now as the most powerful agent of Russia in the Middle East. On the other hand there was the political value of aid for the dam as a counter-stroke to the Czech arms and this argument eventually carried weight. The offer was duly made, but whatever altruistic motives inspired it earlier had vanished. The High Dam was caught in the Cold War struggle.

In the event, Nasser did not respond to the gesture, as his refusal to accept the *aides mémoires* of February demonstrated. His relations with the Soviet ambassador grew steadily more cordial and with the ambassadors of Britain and the United States more distant. Britain was faithfully withdrawing her troops from the canal zone in accordance with the 1954 agreement, but this caused little more than a ripple of goodwill in the flowing tide of rancour. Then in May President Nasser recognized Communist China.

No act was better calculated to offend public opinion in the United States or anger Mr Dulles, the powerful Secretary of State. Nasser had deliberately acted in conflict with the central principle of American policy in Asia, and by so doing seemed to confirm the growing opinion in Congress and the Government that there was nothing to be gained by favours to him. Ahmed Hussein, the Egyptian Ambassador in Washington, noting the adverse trend of opinion, hurried back to Cairo, where he sought to convince Nasser that he should accept the offer of loans for the dam at once, before it was too late.

Nasser was slow to be persuaded but at last, after checking with Mr Eugene Black, Director of the World Bank, that the offers of loans still stood, he agreed in July that Ahmed Hussein should return to Washington and accept the *aides mémoires* without further conditions. It was already too late. Mr Dulles announced publicly the withdrawal of the U.S. offer on the grounds that developments since it was made no longer favoured the success of the project, and as the three offers were inter-dependent, the bank and Britain automatically withdrew theirs.

There was no money for the High Dam after all.

An embittered Nasser retaliated by nationalizing the Suez Canal Company, declaring that the profits of the canal would be used to build the dam. This was manifestly impossible, for even if they were enough, there was little likelihood that any international combination of engineering firms would stake their resources on so great an enterprise for a country that, rightly or wrongly, was represented as perfidious and procommunist. The international consortium formed to build the dam was disbanded as soon as financial help from the Western world was withdrawn. The nationalization of the canal company in turn led directly to the Suez crisis, which culminated in the Anglo-French invasion of Egypt.

Instead of getting aid Nasser had a war on his hands, but the irony of the situation was that neither his anger nor the masterstroke of Mr Dulles was justified by the needs of the dam. Egypt had no immediate use for the loans that were withdrawn because the programme of building depended on the Aswan hydro-electric station, which alone could provide the immense amount of power required for the construction, and the station was still far from complete.

The plan for it, which had absorbed so much of the time and thought of Adrien Daninos, had continued to exercise the experts of Messrs. Kennedy and Donkin and the Swedish firm of VBB[1] without the Egyptian Governments reaching a decision. In 1950 they got as far as selecting a plan, calling for tenders and accepting the lowest, but they did not vote the funds. Immediately after the revolution in 1952, the consultants and the Egyptian Hydro-Electric Power Commission selected a new and cheaper plan than the one submitted for tender two years earlier, and this proposal was accepted by the Military Government on November 2. The contract for the civil engineering work and the buildings was concluded in February and this preliminary part of the scheme was duly completed on schedule near the end of 1955. The entire engineering construction of the station was still to be done when the offers of the High Dam loans were withdrawn. Some years were therefore bound to elapse before the major work of the first stage of the dam could begin.

How much time Nasser had to spare is now difficult to estimate with precision because the Suez affair itself imposed delays. French, British, German, Swedish, Swiss and Italian firms were engaged on the hydro-electric project and the French withdrew all their workers. Construction continued with Egyptian engineers in the place of French, but Britain and France cut

[1] Messrs Vattenbyggnadsbyran.

commercial and financial relations, big cranes essential for the work were not shipped from France, and there were continuing difficulties over spare parts required from Britain. These obstacles probably imposed about a year's delay, but even without it the power for the High Dam could not have been available before 1960.

CHAPTER FOUR

Roubles to the Rescue

In 1957 there were brave words and bare cupboards in Egypt. The voices of victory were loud in the land, proclaiming the humiliation of British, French and Jews who had a few weeks earlier boldly entered to take back the Suez Canal and, if truth be known, to overthrow the 'tin-pot dictator' who had impertinently thumbed a nose at the powers. The British and French troops had not stayed long enough to welcome the new year and the Israelis were crawling reluctantly back towards their desert frontier. The United Nations were busy at New York planning to reopen at their expense the canal that the Egyptians themselves had blocked. The war that was never really fought had been won with words 5,000 miles away from the battlefield and President Nasser, tin-pot or clay-feet as he might earlier have seemed, was standing firmly astride his canal.

All the same, the brave new world he had promised his people never seemed more a mirage than it did at this time. If the body-scars were few by the standard of war, emotional wounds left Egypt and its President lamentably weak in friends. The United States, architect by remote control of victory in the war it had helped to start, remembered that it did not like President Nasser after all and was in no hurry to re-establish the economic relations of the previous year. Britain and France, without diplomatic relations and unhappy about the whole affair, were in no mood to accept defeat gracefully and clung firmly to the economic restriction they had imposed on Egypt at the height of the crisis and now hoped to use as counter in the coming bargain over the costs of Suez. Egypt was, therefore, cut off economically from three major powers and, in particular, found it extremely difficult to trade in sterling, her currency in the free markets. This economic struggle lasted longer than the war. President Nasser was forced to ration kerosene, the fuel of the common people, to cut Government expenditure by ten per cent, seize rice stocks to prevent hoarding, throw profiteers into jail, cancel all importations for Government departments and cut most others, and forbid all holidays abroad. The cost of living rose.

The High Dam, touch-paper of all the trouble, hardly bore thinking about. Even the Suez Canal, whose profits were promised to it, was closed for nearly half the year and was hardly likely to contribute anything for some time to come. There was no money in sight. The Russians, who had hinted at help, made it plain that they felt they were doing enough by contributing to the industrial development programme. President Nasser sent envoys as far afield as Japan for the funds he needed but they returned empty-handed. Even the white lines on the cliffs at Aswan began to fade in the sun. The public image of the dam became less solid under the impact of these extraneous events. The momentary hardness imparted by the promise of money was lost; it acquired the character of a legend projected into the future instead of the past. There was official talk about it, newspapers wrote about it, budgets set aside money for it, but not many people outside the presidential circle believed in it any more. It was no longer just a question of money. There was also the question of the Sudan, that neighbour country which would lose one of its main towns and a hundred-mile strip of land under the waters of the dam; its assent, so long taken for granted despite protests from Khartoum, suddenly seemed less likely. And then, were the experts right about it? Dr Abdel Aziz Ahmed, chairman of the Egyptian Hydro-electrical Commission and one of the country's ablest engineers, stated publicly in August that a dam at Wadi Rayan, 60 miles south-west of Cairo, would be much better and cheaper. Was this not a hint from on high that the concept of a High Dam at Aswan was fading? It was true that at this time the Egyptian mission was sounding-out the Japanese about finance for the dam, but was this journey to the end of the earth not also a despairing journey to the end of a dream?

Some of these doubts were engendered by Western opinion embittered by Egypt's success in the Suez affair. There were people in Western Europe and the United States who hoped that the project would fail and found it easy to exaggerate the difficulties it would encounter if ever it were embarked upon. With few exceptions, references in newspapers and magazines, losing sight of the fact that great German firms had designed and world experts had approved it, concluded that the scheme was unsound. The normal difficulties encountered in an enterprise of such magnitude were portrayed as insurmountable.

There could be little doubt that any fault in the design that led to a break in the dam, either by the weight of water or an atom bomb, would cause a disaster greater than any witnessed by mankind. Egypt would, to all intents and purposes, disappear, leaving behind only its nomads and distant oases, its canal zone and those people in the valley who were miraculously able to escape to the desert and survive there. Of Cairo, only the casino on the Mokattam Hills might be left with a belly dancer gyrating to the drumming, strumming fluting of the '*taht*', and a handful of characters, whose luck had survived the greatest chance of all, playing baccarat in a back room. Even the experts admitted that an atom bomb would produce a disaster of unparalled dimensions if it struck the dam without prior warning, and the reply of the Egyptian Government could only be that to presume the nuclear strike was not far from presuming the end of the world.

But the idea of calamity-by-flood was less potent in the public mind than other criticisms. Most people were prepared to assume that the world's engineers and the Egyptian Government were not in league with lunacy to hazard their utter destruction. The converse opinion, that there would not be enough water in the reservoir, was a more compelling and insidious idea. It was contended by critics that the water would float away to heaven by evaporation, seep down through the sand to the western desert, or simply escape through a gap in the western hills to the Red Sea. This last opinion, which eventually found its way into the columns of the now-defunct *News Chronicle* of London, contended, in effect that the geographers who studied the Nile basin south of Aswan were imbeciles incapable of reading the data that all the facilities of modern science had put at their disposal, and it might be counted among the wilder flights of critical fancy.

Other arguments favouring failure depended so much on mathematical and technical detail that they were beyond the comprehension of the layman but were able to influence him. The contention that the river would lose water to the desert was based on records which showed that the Nile water available in the first fifty years of this century was less than in the preceding half-century. It was claimed that the decline was not due to less rainfall in the African mountains but to the failure of an underground supply. In 1898 Dr John Ball had reported that a large amount of underground water from the desert reached the Nile between Aswan and Wadi Halfa from the desert, and that there were 375,000 square miles of rock, mainly sandstone, stretching from Egypt and the Sudan into Libya, which contained 22 per cent of their volume in water drawn all the way from the Chad highlands. In the opinion of Dr Abdel Aziz Ahmed, this subterranean 'lake' had supplied the Nile until 1902, when the first dam was built, since when the supply had not only ceased but had been reversed by seepage from the river to the Libyan oases. He calculated that between 1912 and 1933 there had been an annual loss to the Nile of between 8 and 6·5 milliards of cubic yards of water annually, and that there had been a simultaneous increase in the water available in the oases of Libya; in short, the dam, by the pressure it exerted against the flow of the Nile, had forced it to lose this quantity of water at a time that it was only storing between 3 and 6·5 milliards.

Dr Abdel Aziz believed that the water-holding capacity of the rock beneath the desert was almost limitless and, therefore, that the High Dam would have the same effect as its predecessor. It would force water out to the rock; but on a greater scale. He reckoned that for the first twenty years after the building of the dam, the Nile would lose its entire discharge of 110 milliards. The silt would meanwhile be sealing the banks, and for the next ten years the loss would average 51 milliards annually. Only after this decade would Egypt and the Sudan get the use of 15·5 milliards more than they do now. In short, there would be a loss of water for thirty years and thereafter a minor gain.

The belief that the lake behind the dam, situated in one of the hottest and most arid regions in the world, would lose too much water by evaporation to justify the benefits claimed for it, was an inevitable and general criticism of the project. From past experience, and the results of tests with basins containing measured quantities of water at Aswan, the conclusion was reached that the lake would lose 13 milliards every year, but many critics considered this estimate too low. Dr Abdel Aziz, again, was one of them. He argued that the greater wind velocity experienced at the higher level of the water when the reservoir was full would increase the annual evaporation by 5 milliards, that is, to an estimated 18 milliards.

Dr Abdel Aziz contended that the High Dam was ill-conceived and possibly the worst method of attempting to achieve the ends in view. He did not deny that a much bigger reservoir was needed at Aswan to provide over-year storage, but he argued that this should only be part of the development of the Nile basin as a whole. In essence, he wanted the oldest plan of all: the use of the African lakes and a canal through the Sudan swamps. The lakes, he pointed out, would be compensated for evaporation by rainfall, and the canal through the swamps would release large quantities of clear water for the Sudan and Egypt. Drawing on his experience as a hydro-electrician he proposed that the water should be boosted through the swamps by electrical pumps.

He also favoured the old Wadi Rayan scheme, as improved by modern techniques, for over-year storage. It had for long been suggested that Wadi Rayan, a depression adjoining the Fayoum oasis about sixty miles from Cairo, should be linked to the Nile by a canal, which would become an escape channel for the flood. Each year, by this canal, about 2·5 milliards of cubic yards of water could be recovered for irrigation by natural flow when the river level fell. Later it was proposed that another 2·5 milliards could be recovered by pumping from the Wadi some of the remaining water. Then in 1947 Dr Abdel Aziz suggested that the power of the hydro-electric station being designed for the old Aswan Dam could be used in conjunction with free-flow to provide no less than 10·5 milliards during the period from February to July, the period when power could be spared from the station. In those days, 10·5 milliards was reckoned to be the amount needed to extend summer cultivation to an estimated limit of 7·1 million acres.[1]

There was little reason to question the value of Dr Abde Aziz's proposals for Wadi Rayan and the Sudan swamps, both of which will have their place in the eventual development of the Nile, but in advocating Wadi Rayan in 1957 he was making a frontal attack on the High Dam scheme, being a prophet of doom. He considered it a fanciful idea, foreign to Egypt, and constituting a complete reversal of the time-honoured irrigation policy of the Nile: it would, he wrote later, 'be unwise and extremely hazardous' to build it. Certainly the dam would be a disaster if his calculations were correct. The country would, over a decade, waste a great part of its substance, incur massive debts that future generations would have to meet, and, during thirty years of explosive population growth, have less water to irrigate less land. In place of the glorious rebirth promised by the revolution there would be a withering away in deepening poverty.

There will always be those who cry havoc on great enterprises. When the French traveller, M. de Guerville, was looking with awe on the first dam at Aswan in 1904, a celebrated archaeologist told him:

> 'It is an error, a terrible error . . . The English engineers will not admit the possibility of constructing a barrier on any other foundation than rock. They therefore chose the actual site because the bed of the Nile at that point is rocky; but the Aswan rock is only hard on the surface, this hardness coming from the action of the water; underneath it is soft, in a way rotten. For two years, under the continual pressure, the rock on which the foundations rest has sunk, and the

[1] Dr Abdel Aziz Ahmed was primarily a hydro-electric power specialist and became engineer-in-charge of the construction of the Aswan station which, ironically enough, proved vital to the construction of the High Dam. There were, of course, many other critics of the High Dam project, notably in the Sudan, but as a member of the Institution of Civil Engineers, with nearly half a century of experience of work on the Nile, his opinion carried weight. It was, furthermore, most coherently expressed in two Papers presented to the Institution in London on November 15, 1960: No. 6102, 'Recent Developments in Nile Control'; and No. 6370, 'An Analytical Study of the storage losses in the Nile Basin, with special reference to Aswan Dam'. He returned from London to Cairo after, it was said, confessing to President Nasser that he was wrong. He was already past retiring age and went on pension.

dam itself has already shifted about eight feet. My opinion is that it will not last, and unless it is decided to abandon it, and create several smaller barriers, the world one of these days will witness a most fearful cataclysm.'[1]

The confident scholar has long since taken his promise of doom to the grave and the dam has with unflinching calm withstood every pressure imposed on it by the river. If his jeremiad seems ridiculous now, he was not alone in his day, and, later, there were those who said each heightening of the dam would bring disaster. Even in this last decade a great controversy raged among the experts, some of whom contended that the vibrations set up by a hydro-electric station at Aswan would rattle the old dam to pieces. The layman, not equipped to measure the conflicting evidence, was bound to assume that the critics of the High Dam were as likely to be as wrong as all the jeremiahs who had gone before; at least their evidence had been available to all the experts who created and approved the project. But it was symptomatic of the pervasive doubt, the lack of faith in the High Dam, that Dr Abdel Aziz should confidently advocate a better alternative.

Nevertheless, for President Nasser, born with all the stubbornness and patience natural to the Saidi of Middle Egypt, there was no doubt it could and would be built. In the summer of that first desperate year after Suez, he allocated £E2,750,000 from his hard-pressed budget for preparatory work at the dam, although to east or west there was not a penny of aid in sight. The first fragmentary road began to creep south towards a rocky wilderness empty of everything but hope. 'Khawaga, there will soon be a great dam there – a mountain of a dam': the words of the dragoman were themselves acquiring a quality of incantation akin to his stories of Ramses the Second and his glories.

President Nasser had not abandoned hope of getting aid outside the Soviet *bloc* even though Britain, France and the United States were out of the count. From the very start he had conceived the dam as a monument of international co-operation, a monument to a form of neutrality in world affairs which, interpreted in his own way, had become the principle of his foreign policy. He turned to Japan without much expectation and his

[1] M. A. B. de Guerville, ibid.

disappointment was therefore not hard to bear, and for a time a group of Italian industrialists were interested in the project. The tentative proposal of a West German consortium to contribute a $47 million credit was the most promising offer of aid. By this time President Nasser had begun to repair his fences with the United States and the State Department was trying to restore the interest of the West German Government in the dam which, after all, its engineers had designed. There was, nevertheless, insufficient aid from the West to ensure the building of it.

The economy of Egypt was meanwhile steadily drifting towards Russia, driven by the debts incurred for arms, seduced by Soviet *bloc* purchases of cotton and held to its course by the restrictive measures of the Western powers. In 1957, the Soviet *bloc* took 50 per cent of Egypt's foreign trade, five times more than in 1956. In his anxiety for the dam, President Nasser was willing to take Russian aid: but the Soviet Government, far from satisfied that the rift between Egypt and the United States was real, and unwilling to take a spectacular step that might encourage the Western powers to bury their Egyptian hatchet, was in no hurry to offer it. In November, Field Marshal Abdel Hakim Amer obtained a loan in Moscow for £E62 million, on the very advantageous terms of 2½ per cent with repayment starting only after the fifth year, but statements in Moscow at the time made it clear that the Kremlin's interest in Egypt's industrial development plans did not extend to the High Dam.

Five years had now passed since the Free Officers had called for designs from Germany and three since the Anglo-Egyptian agreement opened the door to financial aid, but the project seemed as far from fulfilment as ever. In the circumstances, the discussions behind the scenes in Moscow and in Cairo acquired new urgency. The industrial programme, which Russia had agreed to support with money and technicians and for which the first consignments of equipment were already arriving in Alexandria, would not be worth much if the power resources of the High Dam were not eventually available. On the Egyptian side there was no longer the demand that sufficient aid should be committed to complete the dam, or for an international consortium to execute the work.

There can be little doubt that the Russian Government was only willing to help if the dam could be a Soviet triumph, executed with Russian equipment and by Russian engineers. The more pressing the Egyptian need became, the nearer President Nasser moved towards the terms Russia required for participation in the scheme. They were terms that President Nasser had never been willing to grant the Western powers, but the pressure of time, of events and of the actions of the powers themselves, compelled him to accept them. He might by greater foresight have seen the outcome of his policies: equally, history will record that Anglo-American policies not only transferred the achievement to Russia, with all that meant as an example to the underdeveloped regions of Africa and Asia, but forced Nasser to accept terms tying him to the commitment.

In October, 1958, the Soviet Government offered to finance the High Dam and in December a basic contract was concluded with the Egyptian Government whereby the Russians would provide 400 million roubles (about $92 million) repayable over twelve years, beginning in 1964, at 2½ per cent. This was for the first phase of construction, to consist of cutting the channel on the east bank to divert the Nile and the building of the upstream and downstream coffer dams, providing water storage to a height of 140 yards. The text of the agreement, however, gave the Soviet Government a virtual veto over the use of any foreign contractors by specifying: 'The implementation of the work will be entrusted to contractors in the manner to be agreed by the two sides, on the basis of the use of Soviet equipment.' Even if West German or Italian firms had been willing to participate in the new conditions, this clause effectively excluded them from the use of their own or other familiar equipment. Russia had effectively secured control of the project and nothing more was heard of other foreign participation in the first stage of construction after the visit of representatives of the German consortium in January 1959.

Even before the contract, and without waiting to see whether the Russians would accept the Hochtief-Dortmund design, the Egyptian High Dam Committee allotted $1,960,000 for immediate work on the roads, railway and electricity supply routes to the site. As soon as the contract was signed, the German design was taken to Moscow for restudy and when the blueprints were returned to Cairo in May, 1959, some major changes had been made. Their main proposal was to erect the power station at the central tunnels of the diversion channel instead of in tunnels specially dug for the purpose on the other bank. Their design also shortened the north–south length of the dam. They proposed to quicken the work of sand-filling by using a method of sluicing the sand into position, which had been used successfully on Russian rock-filled dams. Briefly, this method consists of filling a basin of sand with water then pumping the resulting sand-paste through pipes to the site of the filling.

The international board, which studied the Soviet plans in the second week of June, 1959, advised strongly against the proposal to site the power plant in the tunnels of the diversion channel, and requested that entirely independent power tunnels should be sited on the west bank. They agreed that the north–south length of the dam could be reduced but suggested that the rock barrier in the centre of the diversion channel – through which tunnels were to be driven – should be increased from 200 metres to 300 metres. Finally, the board opposed the Russian method of sand-filling by sluicing. This report put the Egyptian High Dam experts in difficulties, but the two Governments, without waiting for the technical disputes to be settled, concluded and signed their final agreement by which Russia would provide the plant, equipment and engineering assistance for the first stage. The Russians then refused to have any more advice from the International Consultants.

Eight Russian engineers left Moscow at once for Aswan and Soviet heavy equipment was loaded on ships for Alexandria. It was, for President Nasser, a political victory equal to that of Suez; bought perhaps on terms he did not want to pay but nevertheless a victory. The money had at last begun to flow, the wheels at last to turn, for the greatest constructional enterprise in a country which had been famous for them in antiquity.

One obstacle yet remained: the Sudan. The end of the beginning of the High Dam story was in Khartoum.

CHAPTER FIVE

Soldiers' Salute

Although the High Dam is being built more than 200 miles inside Egypt, its water will reach back along the Nile valley to a point about 100 miles inside Sudanese territory and submerge almost the entire inhabited region of Sudanese Nubia, including the frontier town of Wadi Halfa. Fifty thousand Nubians are doomed to lose their homes and farms before the completion of the main dam because the upstream coffer dam will raise the water above the Nubian valley stretch of the Sudan. It was, from the outset, unthinkable that Egypt would drown her neighbours. In any case, Egypt and the Sudan shared the Nile waters in accordance with an agreement reached in 1929 and the acquired rights could not be changed except by mutual consent. The dam was obviously going to make a radical change.

The Sudan had therefore an effective veto on the plan and the Anglo-American offer of aid had included the proviso that Egypt should come to terms with her. The Russian offer must have contained a similar condition, but when the contract was signed between Russia and Egypt, the Sudan was in no mood to accept the dam scheme, and would not even acknowledge the 1929 agreement on the grounds that it had been signed by Britain and Egypt and allowed no water for the expansion of Sudanese agriculture. The Egyptian Government, on the other hand, would not discuss a new agreement unless the Sudanese would accept the existence of the old. There was little prospect of negotiations much less accord.

The tactlessness of the Egyptian leaders did not help. They mentioned the High Dam project to the Sudan Government in 1952 and then for two years left Khartoum officially in ignorance of progress while they talked publicly about it. The Sudanese were not impressed by the Egyptian argument that details could not be given of a scheme that was not yet formulated. They felt that they were being treated with high-handed disregard for their interests and this engendered a prejudice that was slow to fade. And the Egyptians *were* high-handed. They were so imbued with the belief that Egypt's sovereignty over the Sudan was a natural and inevitable thing, desired by the Sudanese, that a veto on the High Dam was unthinkable.

At the time of the revolution the Sudan was still theoretically a condominium governed jointly by Britain and Egypt, a form of rule which had its first symbolic expression when Kitchener hoisted the flags of both Britain and Egypt over Khartoum after defeating the dervish army at Omdurman in 1898. The British had in practice ruled the country through its Governor-General, its Sirdar in command of the army, and its officials, and for the greater part of the time had been helped to rule by British proconsuls in Cairo. The Egyptians considered that the Anglo-Egyptian conquest of the Sudan had restored Egyptian sovereignty, and negotiations with Britain over Egyptian independence had repeatedly broken down on their claim. The pre-revolutionary Wafd Government, without consulting Britain, proclaimed Farouk King of the Sudan in 1951, an act which delighted the Egyptians but suffered from the slight defect that there were no means of enforcing it. The revolutionary Government showed more realism by dropping the Wafd claim and, as a result, were able to agree with Britain and the Sudan that the Sudan would get its independence, but in doing so they really believed that they were merely clearing the way for the unity of the Nile valley at the will of the two peoples. The opinion seemed justified when the first elections brought to power Ismail al-Azhary, a life-time proponent of union, but, in the event, Azhary was hardly on speaking terms with Nasser by 1955 and it was he who declared the total independence of the Sudan. An anti-unionist Government under Abdullah Bey Khalil was ruling the Sudan in 1958.

The cavalier attitude of the Egyptian Government to the Sudan in the early stages of planning the High Dam reflected, in short, the belief that they would soon be ruling 'the south', but when the blueprints were ready and the question of raising funds was becoming urgent, even they could see that the Sudan was unlikely to become a province of Egypt; an agreement about the dam was, after all, going to be necessary

The Azhary Government was in no mood to compromise when the first negotiations on the dam began in 1954, being annoyed because Egypt had allotted money for the project in the budget without giving the Sudan any information about it. They saw the scheme in detail for the first time only when the talks began in September, and as they considered it a project prepared by Egyptians for Egyptians, they were further annoyed to see it described as a 'joint scheme'. The Sudan Ministry of Irrigation commented:

> 'The Egyptian Government had already repeatedly announced that they were going to build the Sadd el-Aali, and the Sudan Government had every reason to take offence at the lack of politeness which Egypt had shown in announcing her intentions without consulting the Sudan. . . . Under international law the Sudan Government has an unquestionable right to veto the Sadd el-Aali project, and she will do so unless her interests are properly safeguarded before the work starts'.[1]

As Egypt did not dispute the need to compensate the Nubians, the interests that the Sudan desired to protect were her future claims to Nile water and the right to build controls on the river to make use of the water. The Sudan was using about 5 milliards of cubic yards of water every year as against Egypt's 63 milliards, and these were the 'established rights' from an agreed annual flow measured at Aswan of 110 milliards. The object of the discussions was to re-divide the 110 milliards in proportions that would meet the expected future needs of both countries, but the bases of their respective claims conflicted. Sudanese experts argued that the factor limiting the development of their country was water, not land, and that if its needs were measured either by land area, or by population in proportion to Egypt's population, the Sudan should have about one-third of the annual flow. They admitted it would be many years before the Sudan could make use of so much water but they wanted the share defined in advance so that Egypt, with her greater potentialities for control, would not continue to 'establish' water rights at the expense of the Sudan. The experts also disagreed about the amount of

[1] *The Nile Waters Question*, published in 1955 by the Sudan Ministry of Irrigation and Hydro-Electric Power.

additional water that the dam would make available. The Egyptians contended that the Sudan was claiming so much that Egypt would have to sacrifice some of her existing water, particlarly as the Sudanese wanted Egypt to deduct from her share the full 13 milliards of cubic yards of water which would be lost by evaporation. The experts met again in April 1955 and Egypt then offered the Sudan 14·5 milliards, which was firmly rejected.

In the crucial year of 1958 the relations between the two countries were so bad that they came near to war. In January, another attempt to negotiate agreement on the dam failed dismally on the old issues. Then, a month later, Egypt unaccountably laid claim to 10,000 square miles of desert frontier and the Sudan Government, fired by fierce resentment in the country, began to mobilize. The crisis subsided but the Egyptian claim was not abandoned until June. The Egyptian Government was in turn incensed when the Sudanese filled the new canals of the Managil extension to the Gezira cotton area without consulting Egypt, which gave practical expression to the Sudan's unilateral rejection of the 1929 agreement.

The Sudanese Ministry of Irrigation, which favoured the development of the Nile basin as a unit all the way from the African lakes, had worked hard on a new version of this scheme and rushed it out in 1958 when Egypt was on the point of reaching agreement with Russia on financing the dam.

The starting-point of the scheme was Owen Falls Dam at Lake Victoria, which already existed, and it provided for further dams on Lake Albert and Lake Kioga and at Lake Tana in Ethiopia, with a tunnel connecting Tana with the headwaters of the Balas in order to shorten the flow of the Blue Nile to the Sudan and provide a powerful head of water for generating electricity. It suggested the Jonglei Canal to take the White Nile through the swamps, another dam at Roseires to supplement control on the Sudan stretch of the Blue Nile at present depending on the Sennar Dam, and irrigation at Khasm el-Girba on the Atbara river. Finally the plan provided for three dams on the main Nile between Khartoum and Wadi Halfa and a big dam – although not an over-year storage dam – at Aswan.

The Ministry claimed that 12 milliards of cubic yards of water would be added to the annual flow of 110 milliards by preventing loss of water *en route*, and that after allowing 15·5 milliards for evaporation and 2 milliards for irrigation in East Africa, there would be 105 milliards left for storage in existing or proposed reservoirs, an increase of 36·5 milliards *available for use.* Large amounts of electricity could be generated in Ethiopia and Uganda, one million kilowatts in the Sudan, and 500,000 kilowatts in Egypt at Aswan.

The execution of this project required, as in the case of its predecessors, the agreement of the British East African territories, Ethiopia and Egypt, and the British Government thought – although what Britain thought meant little to Egypt so soon after Suez – that a technical conference of all the states concerned should be held. This in itself was enough reason for Egypt to reject it, for it was highly probable that years would be spent in negotiation even before the work got under way. There was not the slightest chance at this late stage of Egypt abandoning the High Dam project, which would give her control of her own water and, once the finance was available, enable her to set a building time-table. The Sudan scheme was still-born by reason of Egypt's opposition; equally the Sudan could stop Egypt building the High Dam. It was deadlock.

Thus, as the U.S.S.R. and Egypt approached agreement on the first stage of the dam, relations with the Sudan were bad and the bulk of the Sudan coalition was anti-Egyptian. There were, however, elements in the coalition that were intriguing in Cairo and signs of instability began to emerge. In September, the Egyptian broadcasting station unleashed a virulent campaign against the Khartoum Government and the Sudanese Prime Minister claimed to have knowledge that the Egyptian Government were in league with some of his ministers to bring him down by a *coup d'état*. It was, indeed, becoming essential to President Nasser that Abdullah Bey Khalil should fall if the imminent financial agreement with the Russians was to have value. Abdullah Bey decided to forestall his fate by his own *coup d'état*, an astonishing decision that he afterwards regretted. He summoned officers loyal to him to take over themselves and in November an orderly 'seizure' of power took place. The rule of General Abboud began.

It was better luck than President Nasser expected. The Sudanese army contained radical groups akin to those in the Egyptian army of 1952, and it was therefore unlikely that an army régime could follow a rigid anti-Egyptian policy. There were, furthermore, many Sudanese officers who had links of friendship with the Egyptian leaders, forged in the years they served together and shared anti-British sentiments. President Nasser, quickly and correctly assessing the situation, was the first to recognize the Abboud Government, and he was rewarded with a message from the General saying that the Sudan was not opposed in principle to the High Dam scheme.

The negotiations were in due course resumed under much more favourable conditions, and arithmetical divergences underwent a steady process of adjustment even in the minds of the men who had originally created them. The Sudan Government, still intent to secure enough water but no longer determined to oppose the High Dam, settled down to steady bargaining which took several months to complete. The final settlement was not reached until November 8, 1959, when it was agreed that the United Arab Republic – as Egypt now was – would take 72 milliards of cubic yards of water, and the Sudan 24 milliards. In effect, the two countries had agreed to share the loss of 13 milliards of evaporation. The Sudan won the right to proceed with its own Nile control programme and the U.A.R. agreed to pay the Sudan £E15 millions for the resettlement of the Nubians. (The dam at Khasm el-Girba, scheduled in the Sudan scheme, was built to provide an irrigated resettlement area for the Nubians on the Atbara river, and the Sudan Government went ahead with the Roseires Dam project).[1]

For Egypt, the Nile Water agreement of November 8 was decisive. It was signed only eleven days after the conclusion of the contract with the Russians for the financing and building of the first stage of the High Dam, and it removed the last obstacle to the start of the work. On January 9, 1960, almost eight years and nearly 4 million new Egyptians after he had decided to

[1] The World Bank and the International Development Association, the specialized agencies of the U.N., agreed in 1961 to make $32·5 million available for the construction of the Roseires Dam, on the Blue Nile, 60 miles downstream of the Ethiopian border. It will double the supplies of irrigation water in the Sudan during the period of seasonal shortage.

embark on the great project, Gamal Abdel Nasser, by this time president of the United Arab Republic and older by a campaign against his régime, an attempt on his life, and the invasion of his country, laid the foundation stone at the first cataract just south of Aswan town. On a high promontory overlooking the river, a simple, inscribed tablet laid where his feet were set at the historic ceremony, records the occasion, much as the triumphs of antique pharaohs are engraved on stone all the way along the banks of the Nile.

CHAPTER SIX

To Build on the Sand and Endure

The High Dam is being built across the Nile between two short valleys, Khor Agama and Khor Kundi, which descend the east bank at right angles to the river near the head of the first cataract, which is about 680 miles south of the sea, 590 miles south of Cairo, and 40 miles north of the Tropic of Cancer. The banks rise steeply 110 feet above the river; yellow on the west bank with sand that rolls away across Africa; jagged with black and brown granite on the east bank where most of the work has so far been done.

There is water only in the river. The rains of the Atlantic and Indian Oceans and the Mediterranean Sea, that enrich the distant world, never reach Aswan. Through the daylight hours of almost all the year an unshadowed dome of blue sky oppresses it with relentless heat from which there is neither shelter nor escape, but within the cycles of month and year there are warm still nights splendidly lucent with moon and stars.

The site is utterly barren. The rocks of the east bank, debris of geological ages, are scorched embers of the world, and, like a huge dead hearth, were empty of sight or sound before work started on the dam. Here, where history of human society is known as far back as anywhere, people have always wondered at the desolation and passed by; slaves and servants came briefly and perforce but no man lived by choice. They found sanctuary here and there in this harsh world only where river beaches gave root-hold for crops.

The choice of this site for the dam was determined by the amount of water it was necessary to impound to make Egypt independent of the annual flood. The old dam had carried the yearly control of the Nile to its limit without altering the country's dependence on the flood and the only way to advance beyond this position, to secure independence of the river's vagaries, was to impound enough water for several years.

Daninos had remarked the existence of a very large natural basin to the south of Aswan town capable of providing 'century storage' if the gap caused by the Nile in its northern rim were closed. An aerial survey with five-metre contours confirmed the truth of the Daninos claim and it remained then only to choose the most suitable location within the agreed site.

The Nile has cut a deep trench through the rainless region stretching from Khartoum to Aswan. Its journey lies through an extensive sandstone plateau, which is broken at intervals by granite that has crystallized and hardened through the ages and tilted in the toughest of layers. These jagged interludes in the sandstone wilderness form the cataracts or natural gateways, where the valley narrows between cliffs and islands of broken stone past which the river froths and tumbles. It is at these clefts, where the river is narrow and the rocks hard, that engineers seek to found their dams. North of the Egyptian frontier they have always been interested in two points: Aswan and, about forty miles to the south, Kalabsha.

Bab el-Kalabsha, a gateway of dark, shining rock narrower than the valley at Aswan, has always seemed a most natural site, but it was rejected for the High Dam as it was for the old. In the first place, it would reduce the length of the reservoir inside Egypt by forty miles. Secondly, the land falls away from the Kalabsha gateway to such an extent that the wings of the dam would need to stretch for four miles across unstable sandstone on each bank of the river, whereas the valley at Aswan was less than four miles from hill to hill and the banks consisted of hard, igneous rock. Aswan had other advantages. It was linked by road, rail and telegraph to Cairo and the Egyptian ports, and the hydro-electric station at the old dam was a necessary source of power for the work of construction. Eventually, the matter of site was determined in 1954 by the international board of consultants, called in to assess the project, by their decision that the upstream defences of the dam, the safe construction of which was essential to the success of the whole scheme, could be built with less hazard at Aswan than in the more turbulent region of Kalabsha.

In 1952 the Egyptian Government asked Hochtief and its associates to design a dam that would give the country complete control of the seasonal and annual flow of the Nile and at the same time give a constant supply of electric power during any one year. The broad objective therefore was to close the northern rim of the natural basin with a wall so big that the surplus of any annual flood could be retained behind it for use in any future years when the flood was low, so that, in the words written prophetically by Sir Winston Churchill more than half a century earlier, the Nile would 'perish gloriously and never reach the sea.' Then, irrespective of the size of the annual flood, a measured 63 milliards of cubic yards of water could be released each year from the reservoir and fed through the old Aswan Dam, and the other barrages and regulators on the Nile, to the farmlands of Egypt.

The plan to let the reservoir fill slowly flood by flood was not as straightforward as it seemed because the behaviour of the Nile, in the irregularity of its supply of water over the years, is something of an enigma. When the German experts began work in 1952 they had at their disposal records of the Nile dating back to pharaonic times and the detailed work done by Hurst, Black and Simaika and their predecessors. Dr Hurst calculated that if one took account of the additional water requirements of Egypt and the Sudan, the earlier twenty-year Nile development programme for century-storage might not meet all the need in twenty-nine years out of seventy-five and that the most drastic economies in the use of water might still leave seven years of short supply. In short, he agreed with Joseph on the danger of seven lean years, and if he would not be prepared to prophesy that those seven lean years would come in succession, he would not equally swear that they never could. It might be unlikely, but there could be a sequence of years in which the reservoir 'ran dry' as far as over-year storage was concerned, or equally a sequence when it would need skilful handling to prevent it from blowing its top in the literal sense. First calculations suggested, in fact, that a reservoir containing 430 milliard cubic yards would be necessary and a natural basin of such capacity did not exist behind Aswan or anywhere else on the main Nile. It was only after statistical and mathematical studies over an even longer period of time that it was reckoned that a capacity of 170 milliards would do. Such a reservoir would give live storage (that is, of water free for use) of 92 milliards, storage capacity for another 39 milliards as a protection against floods, and hold 39 milliards of 'dead' water as a trap for silt brought down from the African highlands. Ninety milliards at Aswan was considered enough for both power and agriculture, making it unnecessary to worry any more about the promise of plenty or penury in the annual flood. Joseph's advice to Pharaoh could be translated into storing water instead of grain. Hochtief-Dortmund's task was to design a dam big enough to store this amount of water at a site predetermined, within a mile or two, by geography.

It was, furthermore, already known that the bed of the river was glutinous and unstable to a great depth over the stretch where the dam must be built and there was nowhere a line of solid granite as foundation. The High Dam had therefore to be of the rock-fill type made possible by the relatively new science of soil mechanics. This meant, in effect, that it would be necessary to construct an artificial piece of the earth's crust in the form of a ridge that would entirely block the valley; a ridge that would lie without foundations, inert and immovable, against the southern face of which the sand and silt of the river would reform themselves in natural layers. The dam would be moulded to the ground, distributing its weight over a great area and at no point offering a perpendicular front to the force of the flood.

Hochtief-Dortmund undertook to produce the preliminary design by April 1, 1953, and in a 'blitz' operation assembled the essential – but far from final – topographical and geological facts by mid-January. There was, indeed, a great deal still to do on both counts and Hochtief continued to map the area from the air and make geological tests of the granite banks while Egyptian engineers, working at that time with French specialists, probed the river-bed to find the precise depth and structure of its glutinous mattress. While this work proceeded, the German experts, working in collaboration with an Egyptian committee, sketched the first plan before the end of February and the Egyptian Government received the preliminary design from Hochtief-Dortmund on the appointed day.

Although there were several possible and significant variations in the preliminary design and it was eventually to be altered, it was for the first time possible to see what the great dam would be like. It would be, as foreseen, a ridge of stratified rock-fill and sand half a mile wide lying on the river-bed with its wings thrown out over the granite for one and a half miles on the east bank and half a mile on the west. The flow of the river would be controlled by two diversion tunnels passing under the east wing and four under the west, while another eight tunnels under the east bank would give water power to the proposed hydro-electric station. The essential character of the dam as it is now being built was contained in this first and hasty design.

The purpose of the diversion tunnels was to draw the flood water away from the river channel while the main structure was raised across the bed, and to make this diversion possible coffer dams had to be built upstream and downstream of the main axis. In concrete dams of traditional type, such as the old Aswan Dam, the coffers are destroyed when the dam is built, but in this case it was proposed to mould the upstream and downstream

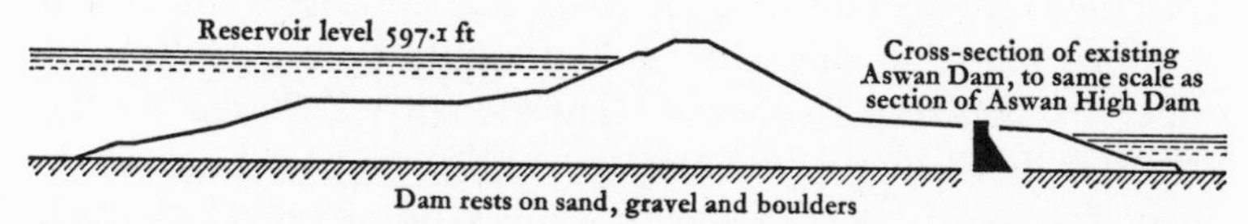

2. An outline cross-section of the dam, with the first Aswan dam superimposed to scale and appearing diminutive by comparison

coffers into the main dam and lay a concrete blanket over them both, so that they would form the northern and southern faces. They would consist mainly of a compacted mass of rock and sand and be bound to each other by layers of rock and clay. The central core, held firm within these man-made strata, would be constructed of clay and strengthened by a horizontal rib of reinforced, plastic concrete below the crest on the downstream side, as protection against the hazards of the wilderness and river and of bombing from the air. The half-mile section of the dam in the river would lie on a thick carpet of dune sand compacted to near solidity by a system of vibration. The dam stood revealed on paper as a monster that would dwarf the old dam which had been the wonder of the world half a century earlier and is still a magnificent sight. Its wings would stretch so far over the banks that its total length would be about two and a half miles and it would rise on a slow incline from the water of the reservoir of the existing dam until, in a later sharp ascent, it reached its peak of 350 feet, and then fall gradually away into the river half a mile to the north.

Defying the biblical parable, the High Dam had to be built on sand and yet endure and, what is more, survive the action of the river on the sand. The bed of the river at this point consists of gravel, rock debris and boulders to a general depth of about 300 feet and at some points of 400 feet. There was no suggestion that foundations should, or could, be laid through this debris to the rock beneath, yet it was evident from the outset that the greatest threat to the stability of the dam existed in this unstable and permeable bed. The river flowing from the south could percolate through the sandy base until it found an outlet and, in doing so, could cause hollow natural 'pipes', which would undermine the dam in course of time.

An orthodox dam is a concrete wall, which rises vertically from the bed-rock and seals the river, but the High Dam was to be 'horizontal', in the sense that it would lie on the ground under its blanket of concrete. The design was based on the principle that water would seep through the subsoil at an angle depending on the size of the grains of sand or gravel. A thick stratum of compacted coarse sand laid beneath the dam, particularly in the area where the seepage might begin, could alter the gradient of the water as it percolated in such a way as to prevent it undermining the dam.

No one could afford to make a mistake about this kind of design or the facts on which it would be based at Aswan, for the stability of the entire structure depended on it. For that reason, a small group of men assembled at Aswan in 1952 with the task of solving the problem of the river-bed. This, the first drama of the High Dam, was played to an empty house before ever a stick of dynamite or a pickaxe bruised the granite. Tourists travelling by steamer between Aswan and Wadi Halfa might have noticed a bungalow, and a stubby little boat looking like a tug that had strayed from its coastal waters and had paused bewildered in mid-stream with its engines running, but these trivia in a scene that was everywhere greatly empty were usually passed without a remark. The bungalow was known grandly as the Laboratory of the High Dam. Inside it, a handful of French and Egyptian specialists were analysing samples of the river-bed and the barge housed the drilling machinery that extracted them.

In 1952 the bungalow stood alone, its granite glistening and its woodwork already blistering beneath the relentless sun of Aswan, overlooking the proposed site of the dam from the west bank. It was in due time to be enlarged and within a decade it was part of a complex of works and buildings associated with the dam, but at the beginning it was diminutive and secretive in the wilderness. There was neither air-conditioning nor comfort for the engineers and chemists who worked there. Each day they drove by car out of Aswan town, passed the head of the old dam, and swirled like balls of yellow smoke along the dirt road through the rocks until they disappeared into the dip hiding the bungalow. They were as lonely in spirit as they were in scientific habitation, for at that time there were very few people talking about the dam, which was not yet the *cause célèbre* of politics, finance, engineering and ambition that it soon became. Very little was known of them or their work: Egyptian newspapers sometimes made brief – and usually erratic – references to them. They were, nevertheless, the first in that army of men who are now constructing the High Dam and they were charged with the vital task of proving that it could with safety be built upon the sand.

Standing on the veranda, which ran along the river side of the bungalow, and looking down to the lonely barge, lilliputian in its spectacular surroundings, it was possible to conceive the work of the laboratory in its correct and spectacular context. It had, otherwise, an unpretentious, dilatory air. Young men, even boys, were tending flasks slowly heating over burners; two machines sombrely brought their iron muscles to bear on rocks to test the breaking-point; other burners simmered away, endlessly it seemed, and untended, to distil water from sand and rock in order to measure their permeability. Around the walls were identical jars, filled with granulated dirt in various shades of grey and yellow, all identified with small hand-written labels, like a housewife's stock of home-made jam; and in the yard and on the veranda there were long, narrow wooden boxes, as though the place were inhabited by a junk man with a passion for only one kind of scrap.

The jars were all dated from their starting-point in 1952 and labelled with the nature of their contents, the precise position of the bore and the depth from which the samples were extracted. The wooden boxes contained cylindrical samples of the alluvial bed of the river, so that one could see the loose sand at the top of the surface samples, and all the various graduations from this looseness, through partial solidity, to the granite of the bed-rock at the bottom of the lowest. The section of the river intended to take the dam was mapped for boreholes in set pattern and the barge probed with hollow drills, extracting the cores for the laboratory tests, from which a picture of the river-bed was progressively drawn.

Here and there among the wooden boxes, without any order apparent to the untrained eye, there were other cores of rock which were consistently solid from top to bottom. They were 'artificial rock', made in the sludge of the river under the direction of experts and extracted by drills. William Kamel Shenouda, who worked in the laboratory from the start, described how they drove hollow, perforated drills through the sandy surface of the river-bed into silt and debris of increasing density, sometimes striking large granite boulders broken from the banks, until they reached the bed-rock. They then injected into the hollow drill under pressure a mixture of 80 per cent Aswan clay and 20 per cent cement, so that it squirted through the perforations, permeating and solidifying the surrounding sand and silt. They succeeded in extracting from injected sites consistent cores of solid, coarse-grained, man-made rock, greyish in colour but having the texture of sandstone. 'These cores show,' remarked Mr Shenouda, 'that we can make the river-bed solid and impermeable.'

Standing on the veranda and sketching on a scrap of paper drawn from his pocket, he described what would happen. The engineers would divide the site into sections and, drilling in set pattern as they worked out from the centre of each section, they would form and blend the artificial rock until, on a line ten yards south of the true axis of the dam, they would make a rock curtain, or, as the engineers call it, a grout curtain, which would be sixty-seven yards wide and stretch from bank to bank. This would not be a foundation. It would be the central defence against the undermining of the dam by percolating water. Mr Shenouda continued his word picture until the mammoth dam, rising in imagination from the river, was seen to be woven into the sandy bed with man-made grey sandstone such as that on which, for lack of a table, he was resting his scrap of paper. Only then, and suddenly, the shabby bungalow, its bare rooms, its glass jars, its burners and steaming pots, and its men doodling endlessly with river dirt, took their place in the vanguard of a great ambition.

The laboratory had not reached this advanced stage of study when Hochtief-Dortmund Union submitted their preliminary design and its experts embarked on detailed studies covering every facet of construction, from tests of materials to be used in it to analyses of the ground on which the dam would be laid. The topography of the immediate region was mapped and the geology of the rocks and soil of the site were examined with every skill available to modern science. The laboratory, reinforced by specialists from the firm of Johann Keller of Frankfurt, intensified their drilling both vertically in depth and on inclined planes, and their tests were supplemented by seismographical methods used in oil exploration. This is based on the fact that rocks and earth of different constitution and texture respond differently to explosions, so that by measuring with minute exactness the subterranean response to controlled explosions the experts can acquire a general picture of deep geological structures. The tests were made with explosions in holes drilled in the bed of the river as well as in the granite banks.

German engineers maintained these studies, in the field and in laboratories in Germany and Aswan, from April 1953 until the October of the following year, while other engineers of the firm worked on several possible variations of the preliminary design. Although the requirements of the Egyptian Government had to all intents and purposes been met by the preliminary plan, that plan had been too hastily produced to give confidence that it offered maximum security at the lowest cost. Three designs, variants of the first, were produced, all of which would provide 'century storage' and the needed hydro-electric power, but each of which solved the question of stability in a different way.

The first proposed to seal the river vertically with a concrete wall built into its bed, which meant that a shorter width of dam base from north to south would do. The second relied for security on a very wide base of the proposed rock-filled structure. The third combined both solutions by proposing a concrete curtain in the bed of the river and a medium width of dam for horizontal sealing.

These three proposals were submitted in October 1954 to a team of international consultants whom the Egyptian Government had appointed to study the Hochtief-Dortmund designs and to the British firm of Sir Alexander Gibb and Partners, who were the government's consultants. The board was headed by Dr Karl Terzaghi of the United States, the 'father' of soil mechanics, and it included Dr C. J. Steele and Dr Lorenz G. Straub, also of the United States, Dr Max Prüss of Germany and Professor André Coyne of France. They accepted the third or 'combined' solution because it offered two lines of defence against the dam being undermined by seepage of water: the extensive horizontal layer of compacted sand, which would divert any water beginning to 'pipe' under the dam, and the vertical cut-off curtain beneath the main structure to seal the bed.

There were from the start, however, grave doubts about the proposed concrete wall as a curtain in the bed of the river. It would need to rise nearly 800 feet from the bed-rock, through the sludge of the river and into the core of the dam itself, and it could only be built in the bed by freezing the moisture in it stage by stage downwards. As each section of the sludge was frozen hard, a section of the concrete wall would be built, so that it progressed down to the bed-rock through the hardened sections. The method had never been applied to a wall of the size contemplated at Aswan and certainly never in a region as hot as Aswan; the very idea of refrigeration on such a scale in tropical temperatures seemed bizarre.

The consultants adjourned their consideration of the plans until they had summoned Professor Mohr, a German specialist in the method. He considered that the wall could be built, that the method was sufficiently advanced for it to be employed even at Aswan, and that no serious mishaps had occurred in its use elsewhere. Dr Prüss, who held firmly to the opinion that only a concrete cut-off curtain could ensure the safety of the dam, accepted Professor Mohr's opinion, but other members of the board were not convinced. They believed that the theory of the construction of the wall could easily be upset by insurmountable difficulties never before encountered in the use of the 'freezing' method. Furthermore, they were far from sure that the wall would be secure even if it were successfully constructed in the river-bed. They pointed out that vertically it would be rigid, while horizontally it would be like a thick, elastic plate responding to the powerful and varying pressures of the river and sediments compressed against it. The core of the dam would move in a downstream direction during the first filling of the reservoir and in doing so the crest was liable to bend. These were difficulties foreseen by the designers, who proposed inspection tunnels inside the wall, an elaborate system for repairing any cracks that occurred under pressure, and a telescopic joint near the crest of the dam to allow movement below it without the dam itself being deformed. Dr Prüss thought these defences would be adequate, but the other consultants were far from sure about the performance of a thick concrete wall under the conditions envisaged: 'Experience has shown that the results of operations without precedent may be very different from what is anticipated', they acidly commented.

With Dr Prüss dissenting, they favoured the formation of an impermeable curtain below the core of the dam by the system of 'grouting' tested successfully at the High Dam laboratory; that is, by solidifying the bed of the river by the injection of mixed cement and Aswan clay as described by Mr Shenouda. Although there were few firms capable of undertaking this specialized operation, it had been successfully executed in river sediments more difficult than those at Aswan. Finally, they rated the safety factor of a grouted curtain higher than that of a concrete wall because it could survive the destruction of the upstream concrete covering and, by preventing the percolation of water beneath the dam, prevent the destruction of the dam itself. The decision was therefore reached that the third design, with a

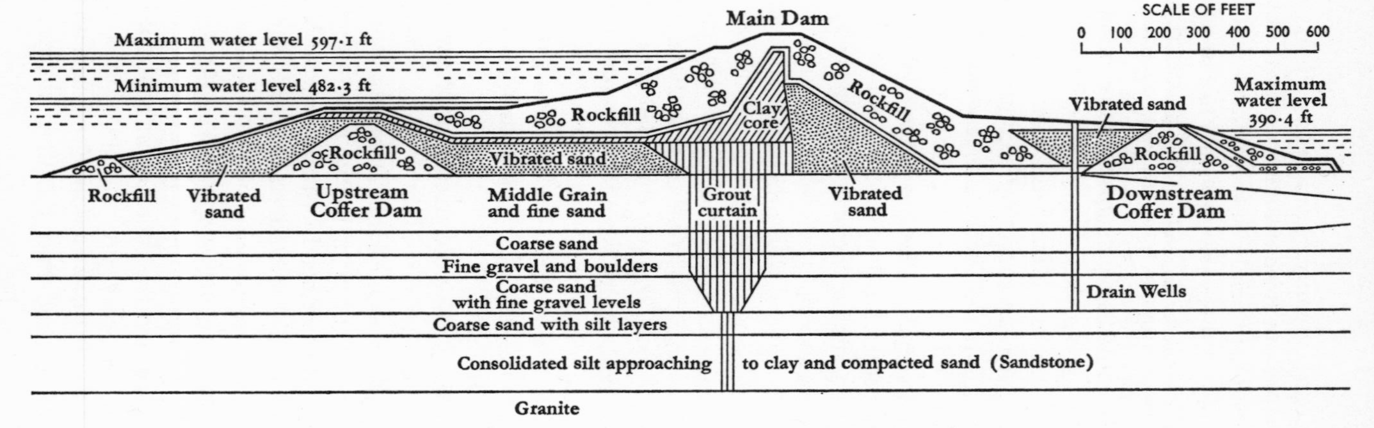

3. A cross-section of the dam, showing the bed of vibrated sand and the clay core contained in its stratum of rocks

grouted curtain instead of a concrete cut-off wall, would be accepted.

The safety of any dam is naturally a primary concern of all designers and consultants but this concern was perhaps more compelling in the case of the High Dam than of any other. The safety of almost the entire nation depended on the correct solution of the problems involved, for, if the dam were to break, its reservoir would engulf the entire inhabited area of the Egyptian Nile valley. The work now in progress at Aswan is based on the conviction that the problems of safety have, with one exception, all been solved.

The exception is danger of nuclear attack. Neither the experts of Hochtief-Dortmund nor the consultants could offer any certain protection against it. The Egyptian Government had asked the designers for maximum defence against air attack and the proposed plastic concrete reinforcement of the crest of the dam was a structural protection. The main defence in the event of war would be, however, the reduction of the level of the water in the reservoir by about 90 feet so that it would not overflow even if the core were damaged. If the horizontal blanket of concrete were damaged upstream of the core, leading to percolation of water through the subsoil of the reservoir, the grout curtain and the filtering arrangements downstream of the core would remain intact and defend the dam against subsidence. But all these precautions, it was admitted, would only be effective against 'bombing by missiles similar to those used in the Second World War';[1] and by that the consultants did not mean the bomb on Hiroshima. 'An atomic bomb could destroy any dam' and defence against it was impossible, the consultants reported.

The Egyptian Government accepted the risk. They were primarily thinking of attack by Israel, which was not then counted as a possible nuclear power, and the consultants were told by the Government representative, Colonel Hilmy, that the danger of nuclear attack was remote. Some people in Egypt maintain to this day that the risk of annihilation is too great to take; but President Nasser contended then and still contends that as the danger applied to almost every creative structure in the world,

[1] The Consultants' report, November 1954.

there would be no planning at all if governments started from the assumption that the world would go mad.

The international board agreed in November 1954 that the dam could be built in accordance with the design and Hochtief then began to plan the building of it. The design approved in 1954 was basic, but it underwent several changes which were incorporated in the 'standard project' completed in August 1955. The 1955 project was in turn modified in accordance with the consultants' recommendations of a deeper grout curtain, more work on the compacting of the river-bed, and additional gravel filling on the downstream side of the core, changes that enabled the designers to reduce the north–south width of the dam by over 900 feet and to shorten the tunnels on both banks. The modifications were of great importance to the security and cost of the project. Finally, the design of the hydro-electric station was altered to provide an output of 2,200 megawatts instead of 1,500 megawatts. But these were all refinements introduced as the costing and the building plan were prepared and did not affect the original decision of the consultants that the mammoth rock-fill dam, the biggest project of its kind in the history of the world, could be built. Only money and a power-supply were needed when, in 1956, the Suez invasion brought planning to a halt.

CHAPTER SEVEN

1960—The Laggard Year

At precisely 13.50 hours on January 9, 1960, President Nasser dynamited 20,000 tons of granite to signal the start of work on the High Dam. It signified his moment of certainty that he was heeled with enough roubles to see him through to the end of the task. Before the month was out the Russians signed a new agreement with him, complementing the first, by which they undertook to advance 900 million roubles (about $226 million) for the second stage of construction.

The Soviet Government made its Technobrom Export Organization responsible for the Russian share of the enterprise and the Egyptian High Dam authority passed to this organization the Hochtief-Dortmund blueprints and the accumulated results of all the research undertaken at the site. The Russian engineers, who were not prepared to build the German dam even though the plans had been modified and approved by a team of top world consultants, began at once to dissect the several large volumes of blueprints which constituted the design and work programme. This, inevitably, brought them into dispute with the Egyptian engineering team who, having helped to prepare the plans, questioned the changes proposed by the Russians. As a result, there were no final plans in existence when President Nasser started the work.

Soviet proposals for changing the design were intended to simplify construction, reduce the time for it and, by these means, reduce the cost and ensure that the limit of aid offered was not exceeded. The Egyptian Government welcomed these aims, for the cost was a great burden and the building of the dam, on which the ultimate success of the country's industrialization programme depended, had already been seriously delayed. The dispute was therefore at the technical level as the Egyptian engineers measured each modification by the standards set by the international consultants.

They did not accept the Soviet proposal to dispense with the grouted curtain beneath the main axis of the dam, on which the consultants had been so insistent. This would have meant broadening the north–south base of the dam in accordance with one of the three schemes put forward by Hochtief-Dortmund and unanimously rejected by the consultants, whose only dispute among themselves had been over the relative merits of concrete and grouting for the cut-off curtain. (The Russians subsequently carried out their own tests on the bed of the river and agreed that the curtain was necessary to the security of the dam.)

Major changes in design were agreed. The Russians contended, with what appears to be a deal of common sense, that as the dam itself could not survive attack by nuclear bombs there was no point in going to the cost of diverting the river entirely through tunnels. They therefore proposed that the river should be diverted through a single, wide channel on the east bank, which would be just over 2,000 yards in length, have a width at bed-level of 66 yards and be sunk about 200 feet from the roof of the plateau. They also proposed that the hydro-electric station should be built on the east bank instead of the west and sited at the downstream end of tunnels which would form the central section of the diversion channel. Thus, the Nile would flow into an open channel 1,148 yards long on the upstream side, disappear into tunnels 312 yards long, and flow back to its own bed through an open downstream section of 547 yards.

Although the international consultants and some of the Egyptian engineers were opposed to this plan to place the hydro-electric station in the diversion channel, it had manifest constructional advantages. The elimination of many tunnels of considerable length, all of which would require reinforcement and concreting, was a considerable saving in difficult and highly-skilled labour. Further, it concentrated the entire diversion operation on one bank, where the full force of men and machines could be assembled, and this was an important factor in quickening and cheapening the work in an area where the only communication between the two banks was by a system of roads which were linked four miles to the north over the crest of the old dam.

To effect the changes in design, the Russians moved the pro-

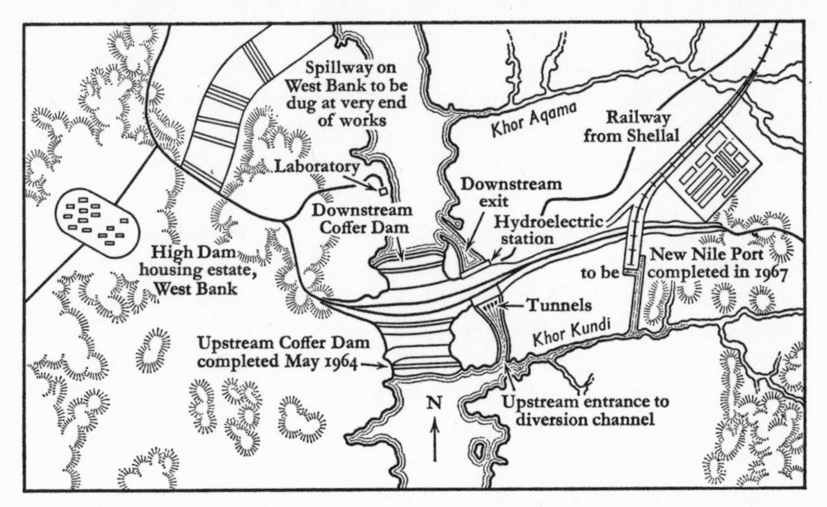

4. The High Dam as it will be when completed, showing the diversion channel with the hydro-electric supply tunnels

posed axis of the dam 600 yards south of the white lines which for several years had beguiled with prophecy the travellers on the Nile. They maintained Khor Kundi as a natural inlet to the diversion channel and took advantage of a depression in the plateau running north-west from the Khor for the line of the channel itself, which turned in an arc to rejoin the river north of the dam.

These changes made no fundamental difference to the design of the dam but they imposed a curve on the long wing over the east bank. The stratified structure of rock and sand filling lying under its blanket of concrete, as designed by the Germans, was unchanged and the final result will look to the layman little different from the dam the Germans might have built.

The first stage of the work inaugurated by President Nasser and now completed, consisted of digging the diversion channel and its tunnels, the installation of control gates at the inlet side of the tunnels, and the building of the coffer dams at the up-stream and downstream ends of the dam. It was essential that, at the appointed date, the coffers would be in position, so that the Nile would rise against the upstream dam, turn eastwards through the diversion channel and resume its natural course north of the downstream coffer dam which would prevent a backward flow on to the dam site. The river between the two coffers would then be left motionless and tranquil for the second stage, the building of the main dam and its fusion with the two coffers.

The first stage was vital to the whole programme. When the international consultants reported on the Hochtief-Dortmund plan they stated: 'The realization of the project of constructing the dam . . . depends on whether or not the waters of the Nile could be diverted into the diversion tunnels without the risk of the failure of the coffer dam which protects the site of the dam against flooding during the period of construction';[1] and one of the principal reasons they gave for building the dam at Aswan was that the depth of the Nile and the force of its flow at that point made the construction of the upstream coffer dam possible. The time-table was rendered extremely rigid by the behaviour of the Nile itself. The target date for the completion of the first step was set for the summer of 1964, and could not exceed by a day the date in July when the Nile flood reached Aswan. If it did so, the work on the diversion channel and the coffer dams would be in danger of destruction and the final structure delayed for a whole year. The loss to Egypt in work and production by such a delay would be in the region of £E200 million.

Even with the most orderly advance planning it was a mammoth undertaking for the four and a half years allotted to it. The diversion channel required the excavation of 12 million cubic yards of solid granite; but this was not all. The building plan was based on using the excavated granite as rock-filling on the dam and its impregnation with sand which was available on the west bank roughly opposite to Khor Kundi and in the desert at Shellal some miles to the north. The 12 million cubic yards of rock excavated from the channel had therefore to be stored at prepared sites and then again transported and dumped accurately, in position and in quantity, in the river. The two coffer dams alone required no less than 6·5 million cubic yards and the upstream coffer required nearly 5 million cubic yards of sand filling.

The work could only be completed in time if excavation took

[1] Consultants' report, 1954.

place simultaneously at the upstream and downstream ends of the diversion channel and in the tunnels. It was, therefore, impossible to wait until the open ends of the channel had reached the length and depth needed to give access to the subterranean section, and this meant that a transport tunnel had first to be dug from the river side at right angles to the line of the channel and sloping to the level of the tunnels, so that excavation could start northwards and southwards on each in turn as the approach route penetrated the section. To obtain the correct gradient and space for the movement of two ranks of heavy trucks, the transport route needed to be 660 yards long with a cross-section of 90 square yards, and this brought the total amount of rock to be excavated to nearly 14 million cubic yards.

Even this colossal task might not have been an extraordinary challenge if an army of men armed with the necessary machines had been ready to wage war on the granite from a prepared base but in January 1960 there was no base, few men and fewer machines, and no power to drive the excavating equipment even if it had been there. Once again the chequered pre-natal history of the High Dam seemed to depend on faith for its survival and for a long time it looked as though faith would not be enough.

The building of any big dam requires the construction of approach routes and communications, the creation of a small industrial town and the marshalling of its working population before any significant progress can be made. In the case of the High Dam, the town, with its factories and workshops, had to be assembled in a rock desert devoid of everything except water to sustain the life of men and machines, and in a pitiless climate where the metal of a machine can blister any hand that touches it during the heat of the day. The labourers had to be summoned from the length and breadth of Egypt and the machines and the greater part of the manufactured materials had to be brought from Russia by ship to Alexandria and moved from there to Aswan by river barge, road or rail. Forty million cubic feet of materials, 95,000 tons of iron work, thousands of houses, hundreds of lorries, trucks, cranes, excavators, pumps, drills, counted in the aggregate in tens of thousands of tons, all were needed, but none was there in January 1960. The first shipload from Russia was at that time on its way to the site from Alexandria.

The fault did not lie entirely with Egypt, unless lack of patience for the slow and orderly preparation of the site is held ultimately to blame. The High Dam project, caught in the complex of political events and denied the foreign funds necessary to execute it, had been so long delayed that when the roubles were ready the order to embark on the work was issued at once. A very small beginning had been made in 1955 when the international consultants approved the Hochtief-Dortmund plan and there was the prospect of Anglo-American finance. A small band of Nubians had then sallied forth from Aswan town, with little more than their muscles to help them, to start work on an access road to the site, and the pick of an unknown Nubian worker, striking its first tiny spark on the granite of the Aswan desert, had signalled the start of the work. The Suez invasion of 1956 and the economic restrictions after it, halted even this diminutive effort, because the Egyptian Government was compelled to be cautious about how much money it spent in the Aswan desert before it knew if it could get the necessary foreign aid to buy the machines and materials needed from abroad. Work was not resumed until Russia had made its offer of aid late in 1958, as Dr Hassan Zaki, chairman of the Sadd el-Aali executive organizations, was subsequently to admit,[1] but even then it was limited by lack of equipment, which could not be obtained until the agreement with Russia was completed and the Soviet engineers had examined and approved the plans for the dam. Only the construction gangs were able to resume the laying of essential branch roads, one of which led to the site of a new and temporary harbour which would enable the river to be used as a supply line. Altogether thirty miles of hard-surface road were laid to form a circulatory system by which men, machines and materials could flow to and from the site, using the crest of the first Aswan Dam as the bridge across the river. This was little to show for the years since the dam was designed but it at least ensured that there were supply lines when the first Soviet equipment began to arrive.

Aswan has been through the ages a frontier town on the edge of the wilderness and even the river, which linked it with the

[1] *The Aswan High Dam*, published by the U.A.R. Information Department, 1961.

Mediterranean, conspired with rock and sand to bar the way south. Until the turn of the century, when the first railway bypassed the cataract to the river-port of Shellal, whence boats ply to Wadi Halfa in the Sudan, the passage of the cataract took two or three days, was dangerous at low water, and required anything from 50 to 100 men to drag and pole the boat past the rapids. The road and rail were extended another two miles south of Aswan when the old dam was built, and the river was bridged for the first time in this region by the dam itself. The site of the High Dam is no more than a step further in terms of the long journey south, but it is a step into the wilderness. Engineers at the old dam have made an oasis rich in trees and flowers to shade their bungalows, but only a few yards to the south the hills of the wilderness close in, man's world vanishes from view, and one seems at once a thousand miles from any living soul. It is just beyond this sharp line drawn between the living and the dead land that the High Dam is being built. No work could begin until the gap, so utterly desolate, was spanned.

The vital access roads ended for the time being in the desert where a handful of engineers and a few hundred Nubians, the first of a great army of men who would eventually assemble, were preparing the site. The Nubians sweated their leisure time in tents or shacks improvised from packing-cases, or took shelter in caves in the granite plateau, and they killed and skinned their sheep for food and slaked their thirst at the river. Every drop of pure water had to be brought by tanker truck from Aswan town.

A ten-mile railway from the old river-port at Shellal was built during 1960. This railway had a long-term purpose in the design of the dam, for it was intended to serve permanently a river-port to be built at Khor Kundi as a new link with the Sudan, but in the meanwhile it had importance as a supply line by which millions of cubic yards of dune sand would be brought from the site as filling for the dam. This railway was a major achievement in itself, for every yard of the route had either to be cut from the rock or laid on a solid granite wall constructed for the purpose.

Progress was also made on other surface installations during the year. A big mechanical workshop was built for the repair of equipment and the construction of many more work buildings got under way. A water tower to serve workers and workshops was nearing completion and dominated the site. Very few houses were built, and the workers for the most part still camped out at the end of the year, but the Russian engineers occupied air-conditioned flats newly built for the Kima fertilizer plant at Aswan.

There was a great deal of muddle, and Russian insistence that the dam should be a splendid and pure example of State enterprise did not help. The U.A.R. Ministry of Public Works and High Dam construction committee had no experience of an operation of this size and had neither organization nor administration commensurate with it. The recruitment and direction of the labour force were so unsatisfactory that within six months the Russians, who might have anticipated that the creaking ministerial machinery would be unequal to the task, were ready to forget their ideological faith in State enterprise and asked for much of the work to be put out to contract. The senior Egyptian engineers, who had seen many earlier works on the Nile built by contract, were in favour of this course and in August of 1960 the Government asked for tenders for the entire work of excavating the diversion channel and tunnels, the concreting, and the building of the coffer dams. It was a crucial decision, and events were to prove that private enterprise might well have been summoned to the High Dam much earlier, to the general benefit of the whole operation.

The engineers of both Russia and Egypt were subjected to great pressure by a time-table of work that had been confidently announced to the world. Hochtief-Dortmund had counted on a ten year building period which provided for the orderly construction of the surface installations, the cutting of the diversion channels and hydro-electric tunnels, and the building of the main dam, all in set stages. Had the Russian planners insisted on this time-schedule everything could have gone according to plan and doubtless ahead of plan, but they believed that the alterations they had made to the design and working techniques enabled them to reduce the building period. They therefore announced that the dam would be built in eight years and the first stage, culminating in the diversion of the Nile, would be completed in 1964.

It seems clear that there was a serious miscalculation of the work involved. Engineer Hassan Zaky, chairman of the construction committee, stated in an official booklet that the diversion channel would be completed in the summer of 1963 and estimated the labour force required 'during certain peaks of construction' at 6,000,[1] whereas with nearly a year of the schedule gone the completion of the channel by 1963 was already impossible and before the stage was finished in 1964 no less than 35,000 workers were at work.

The Russian schedule demanded that excavation and construction of the base should proceed concomitantly but this was impossible in 1960 for the simple reason that electric power was not available. Only machines using oil fuel were at work, and every gallon of oil had to be transported to the site from Sinai or abroad. There was never enough, and in these conditions little could be accomplished at the site. The blasting of 20,000 cubic metres of granite was pointless unless there were powerful machines to dig and remove the debris, so there was very little blasting during the first half of the year.

The only adequate source of power was the hydro-electric station at the old Aswan Dam and it was not yet finished. On January 10, the day after he inaugurated the work at the High Dam, President Nasser threw the switch that turned the first turbine at the station, but the significance of this act, in some ways greater than the ceremony at the dam, made little impression on the public. The output of this turbine was intended for the Kima fertilizer plant, and seemed to have no relation to the dam.

The hydro-electric station had been proposed by Daninos before the First World War; its final design had been approved before the Nasser revolution or the High Dam studies started; work on it was well under way at the time of the Suez invasion and was delayed by it; nevertheless the construction of the station can be considered the most important preliminary work on the High Dam. Without its power, neither the purse nor the determination of any government could have built the Sadd el-Aali because, on the southern rim of Egypt, there was no power

[1] Published by the Department of Information.

for the enterprise and it would have been prohibitive in cost and perhaps logistically impossible to bring enough oil fuel to the site. When Daninos proposed the High Dam as an alternative to the hydro-electric project he was unwittingly putting the cart before the horse, for if the station at Aswan had not existed it would first have been necessary to build it.

Work on the High Dam could not get fully under way until its last turbines started to turn and this did not happen until April 5, 1961. The £28 million station was then able to produce 1,860 million kilowatt hours annually, enough to serve several large towns. About 20 per cent of the power was temporarily allotted to the High Dam and the rest distributed to the fertilizer factory, Aswan town and a sugar plant farther down the river at Kom Ombo. An eight-mile overhead high tension cable from the station to the dam site and two sub-stations to step down the 130,000 volt load to 6,000 volts were built during 1960 in readiness for the power supply. With the exception of the cars, dump trucks and the railway, the power served thereafter almost every operation in the great complex of operations at the site, including the power for the big mechanical excavators which were the key to the excavation programme. The race against time in the building of the dam began in earnest when the last Aswan turbine began to turn.

This had not happened on January 9, 1961, when the first anniversary of the start of the work on the High Dam was celebrated with enthusiasm, some pomp and a great deal of extravagant pronouncements. There was at that time little to celebrate. The surface installations were incomplete, the stores chaotic, the supply line erratic, the labour force too small, and the granite plateau, the giant challenge to the efforts of man, had hardly a scratch on its gnarled face. One year had passed; one of a precious four and a half years in which the great plateau had to be split open to take the whole volume of the Nile flood. Whether they knew it or not, the Egyptians were celebrating that day the start of a crisis at Aswan.

CHAPTER EIGHT

1961 – Year of Crisis

There was nothing to be done for the dam in 1961 but to dig and dump, for of that alone the first part of the first stage consisted. There could be no cementing, or reinforcing, or concreting, and certainly no work on its hydro-electric station, until the work on the open channels or the tunnels had reached their final levels. At this point the engineers could only begin digging the upstream and downstream ends of the open channel and, at the same time, driving the wide transport shaft from the river-side down to the level of the central tunnels.

A notice board at the edge of the plateau overlooking the river marked the axis of the dam and declared it would be the modern pyramid. An Egyptian engineer standing beside this board in January recalled that in volume the dam would be sixteen times greater than the biggest pyramid. 'Everything about this dam is big', he said, almost gloomily as he viewed the desolate scene. 'This year you can say that it is going to be the biggest muck-shifting job the world has ever seen. You've got to get out of your head any ideas you have of a channel or a canal like any you've seen. We're going to carve a canyon right through this plateau right down to the level of the river. In the end, the whole Nile will discharge through the channel and its tunnels at the rate of 300,000 cubic feet a second – that's far more water than flows through any other channel anybody has cut anywhere else in the world. And remember, this plateau we're standing on is solid rock; it's going to take some shifting. We'll do it – we've got to do it – and the channel will be so big that tourists will be coming round just to see the hole'.

To the north-east the water tower in course of construction and the shells of the workshops were visible. There was more activity there than on the plateau, for whereas there was no power from the Aswan hydro-electric station for the digging machines, work was being pushed ahead on the installations.

Even in the town area a lot of excavation and levelling had to be done for roads and foundations. 'The simplest jobs become difficult here', said the engineer. 'To make a little approach road you have to hack your way through granite, and then you have to surface the road because the granite rips the tyres to pieces. Everybody and everything just about cooks in the sun most of the year; it is not bad now, but this is the tourist season, when people come to Aswan for some sunshine and to enjoy the sights. Most of the year the heat of the day is unbearable – just try to imagine a shade temperature of 135 degrees. That's what we had last year and even those of us who are used to working on the upper Nile could hardly stand it. You cannot work during the day in those conditions – certainly not for long'.

The fact remained that the granite and the heat and the size of the plateau were all known quantities in the undertaking before the time-table was set; but a year after the start there was still no power supply, very little heavy equipment, only about 70 Soviet technicians and engineers, about 80 Egyptian engineers and less than 2,000 labourers at the site, and a substantial part of this force was engaged on the ancillary works at the base. Only a few weeks after the first anniversary celebrations Dr Fazyl Kokanbaev and Chief Engineer Ivan Vassilievitch Komzin summoned the members of the High Dam Supreme Committee to a meeting to inform them that work on the dam was not going well. Komzin said bluntly that plans must be revised to increase the speed of the work, and he demanded in particular that arrangements be made to train 1,000 Egyptians at the site in the use of mechanical equipment. He told the newspaper *Al-Goumhouriya* that of the 250 Egyptian mechanical workers already needed only 90 were available. The Egyptian engineers complained that the Russian heavy equipment was also not available and without it the work could not be pushed ahead. The whole operation was caught in a vicious circle: it was no use recruiting the men when the machines were not there to be served, and it was no use bringing machines when there was no power to drive them. When the power from Aswan was switched on in April there were still only three Ulanshev excavators ready for work, no more than one for each sector of the channel.

Reports that the work was not going well were reaching the

foreign Press before Minister of Interior Zacharia Mohieddin, as chairman of the Supreme Committee, started the last turbines at Aswan to provide power for the High Dam. After the ceremony, he toured the site in the company of Musa Arafa, Hassan Zaki and the leading Russian engineers, and at the conclusion of the tour he announced that the armed forces would be called on to provide technicians and mechanics 'to accelerate the work'. Although this clearly implied that the work needed to be accelerated, the Minister proceeded to reply 'to prejudiced propaganda' in the foreign Press, that 'great progress had already been made, especially in the main job: the construction of the diversion channel, of which almost 95 per cent had been completed, despite all difficulties encountered'.[1] Dr Musa Arafa stated in reply to Dr Vittorino Veronese, Director General of U.N.E.S.C.O., that there was no delay, work was proceeding according to plan. Dr Veronese, who was conducting a world-wide campaign to save the Nubian monuments due to be submerged behind the dam, had stated in Khartoum in May that the completion of the dam, would be delayed fourteen months.[2] Even the bluff Mr Komzin was constrained to tell the Press that all difficulties had been successfully overcome.

None of these reassuring statements bore any relation to the truth at the time. There were still only 2,000 labourers at work. They were directed by 120 Egyptian engineers and 80 Russians, but their combined efforts were making little headway. Only 900,000 of the 14 million cubic yards of rock had been excavated, although Engineer Hassan Zaki had earlier estimated that 6·5 million would be dug in 1961, and there was still unrealistic talk of a maximum labour force of 6,000.

The situation was not helped by the deterioration of relations between the U.S.S.R. and the U.A.R. If Krushchev had assumed that Soviet aid for the High Dam would turn the U.A.R. into an obedient satellite he was by this time disillusioned to the point of exasperation by the positiveness of President Nasser's neutrality. The West, judging him largely by U.A.R. voting at the

[1] Quoted in the English language *Press Digest* of the Middle East News Agency of April 15, 1961. References to other statements are taken from issues of the *Digest* in April and May.

[2] Quoted by Reuter.

United Nations and his virulent opposition to most Western policies in the Middle East and Africa, might consider him pro-Russian, but the Soviet Government did not regard him as pro-Russian enough in the right places. His close friendship with President Tito, who was then one of Russia's least favoured heads of state, was heartily disliked; Russia particularly opposed his collaboration with Tito in fostering a *bloc* of neutral states which seemed likely to impede the extension of Soviet influence in the small and emerging nations. Above all, the indigenous communist parties were having a rough time as the Arab revolution spread in the Middle East. This was particularly true of Iraq, and it served to remind Russia that President Nasser kept his communists securely locked up. (He had freed some in 1960 in response to Soviet wishes, but none of any importance.) The Soviet Press castigated the U.A.R. for its anti-communist policy and Mohammed Hassanein Heykal, editor of *Al-Ahram* and confidant of President Nasser, replied firmly that Soviet Russia was one thing, communism another, and Russia should keep its nose out of the internal affairs of friendly states. In June, *Pravda* commented in threatening tone that Egypt should realize that he who paid the piper called the tune.

The Soviet Press had criticized the confusion at the High Dam as early as the summer of 1960 and Egyptian engineers were equally, if less openly, critical of Soviet methods, which they considered inefficient. The political squabble did nothing to improve matters. Although it had no ostensible connection with work at the dam, which seemed to continue as usual in spite of the *Pravda* threat, it increased distrust that was never far from the surface – and this at a time when every effort was supposedly geared to overcome defects of organization and method. The Egyptians suspected that the Russians were deliberately delaying the supply of equipment and they themselves were excessively slow in implementing a training programme agreed in the spring of 1961, reportedly because President Nasser was reluctant to have communists running loose at Aswan in the guise of instructors.

The collaboration of the Russians and Egyptians was difficult enough without these impediments, for they were without a common language and had no experience of working together.

The problem could have been eased if the Russians had allowed the Egyptians to employ some White Russian emigrés, seven of whom had useful experience as well as command of both languages. Egyptian knowledge of the principles governing the High Dam design was to a large extent derived from a Russian called Gregory Tscheborarieff, a former gunner in the Russian Imperial Army who became a disciple of Karl Terzaghi after the revolution and eventually directed the Laboratory of Soil Mechanics at Giza, and there were five available Russian emigré engineers in Egypt, one of whom, Dr Serge Lelyavsky, was rated very highly by the Egyptian experts. The Russians would have none of them.

The methods and language of civil engineering on the Nile were British. The Egyptian engineers had been trained in Western methods and the more senior men had gained their very considerable experience alongside British colleagues on Nile projects. The Minister, Musa Arafa, Chief Engineer Ibrahim Zaki and his deputy, Ahmed Said, had all been associated with the second heightening of the old Aswan Dam and were used to a social relationship which was impossible with the Russians. There were no friendly discussions of difficulties over a drink when the day's work was done; professional friendliness lived at a formal level and problems were discussed stiffly over an office desk. This seemed to be what the Russians wanted. At least they made no effort to change it and, being as sensitive as most Russians abroad to political atmosphere, they became even more remote during the 1961 dispute.[1]

Russian technicians and mechanics got on well enough with Egyptian workers at the site. They travelled together to and from the site in buses, and as they both had a well-developed sense of humour, there was a lot of gesticulatory entertainment on the journeys, but they had nothing else in common and proletarian unity went no further. Nubians in general found the Russians difficult to understand and disappointing. They were bewildered by Soviet groups who arrived by train, manhandled their own baggage to a waiting bus and whirled away to 'little

[1] I asked a Soviet interpreter called Al-Turkestani, 'How do you Russians get along with the Egyptians?' He replied stiffly, 'I do not wish to talk politics'.

Moscow' (as Kima became known) without leaving a piastre behind them. Barmen at the Aswan hotels complained that there was no business from the Russians. Gazing into all-too-empty space they would remark nostalgically, 'The British always bought a drink or two'. Although these were minor factors in the joint enterprise, they added their small quota to misunderstanding.

Soviet participation at the dam was determined phase by phase in a series of contracts which imposed responsibility for a high proportion of the skilled engineering and mechanical work, such as construction and reinforcement of the tunnels and spillway. They manned the powerful diggers and, at the beginning, drove the 25-ton dump trucks, supervised the dynamiting, did all the drilling for erection and blasting, and provided workshop cadres for maintenance and repair work. Although the maximum need for skilled workers was by no means reached in 1961, Chief Engineer Komzin knew how great the need would eventually be and asked for 3,000 Russians. The U.A.R. Government would not accept so large a force, possibly because of the cost, and Komzin then insisted that there should be absolute priority for a large-scale programme for training Egyptians. He blamed Egyptian procrastination over the training programme for the slow progress being made.

The shortage of skilled Egyptian workers was beyond question. It was the well-established pattern of Egyptian society before the revolution and for some time after it that educated people farmed their land or joined the professions. The universities were crowded with would-be lawyers and journalists, of whom there were already too many, while the Faculties of Engineering, which had most to offer the country could not keep pace with requirements. The balance had been corrected to some extent in recent years, and the High Dam recruited engineers from the university as fast as they graduated. It was, naturally, some time before they were of much use, partly because they lacked experience and partly because they were more inclined to abstruse discussion of a machine's capacity than to dirty their hands in making it work. The time had not yet come when grime was regarded as a badge of honour at the dam.

These young engineers could not, in any case, compensate for the lack of men who could retemper a drill head, strip down a gear-box, drive a heavy truck, dismantle and rig; men who could, in short, work effectively on or with the multiplicity of tools and machines which were beginning to crowd the site and its workshops and sheds. The new-comers were valuable as overseers but the High Dam was short of men for them to oversee. Here again the deficiency was historical in origin and bore no relation to the capacity of Egyptian workers, who normally have mechanical aptitude and can improvise better than most. (Time and time again the engineers at the dam were astonished at the ability of illiterate men to fabricate a mechanical part with the simplest of tools and materials.) But even the Egyptian of modest means regarded manual work as beneath his dignity and this was reflected in educational policy which produced an inordinate expansion of university education without adequate expansion of trade schools for training mechanics and semi-skilled workers needed for the Egyptian industrial revolution. Indeed, many of the minor skills had been in the hands of Greeks, Italians and Maltese who left the country after 1956. The Russian demand for a large-scale training programme was reasonable enough.

The Egyptians blamed Soviet inefficiency for delays, contending that the capacity of the Russian equipment for work at Aswan had been overestimated. Drill-heads wore out five times faster than expected and the teeth of the giant diggers buckled and burnt almost as quickly. The engines and gears of the heavy trucks broke under the strain of climbing fully-loaded up steep escarpments and tyres costing $840 each were quickly gashed on the razor-sharp granite edges protruding from the improvised surfaces. The Soviet tyres were still reinforced with cotton which quickly rotted when water penetrated the cuts and were sometimes useless after a single day's work. Perhaps because the consumption of equipment was much greater than anticipated, the Russians failed to keep supplies of machines and spare parts flowing smoothly over the long route from the Black Sea ports, with the result that equipment was often immobilized for long periods of time. By the summer of 1961 the problem was acute, for the breakdowns affected related operations, spreading through the site like a paralysing infection. If a digger was out of action, there was no work for the trucks and the workers assigned to it and time was wasted while they were temporarily switched to other tasks. The Ulanshev excavator, weighing 180 tons and capable of lifting five cubic yards or six tons of rock in its scoop and of loading a 25-ton truck in under two minutes, was old-fashioned in design but excellent in performance, but for any major repairs it had to be sent all the way back to Russia.

The context of these difficulties was the cumbersome control organization of both sides. The Egyptians had no less than three committees, headed by Zacharia Mohieddin, Vice-President and Minister of Interior, Dr Musa Arafa, Minister of Public Works, and Engineer Hassan Zaki, all overseeing the operation with varying, overlapping and sometimes conflicting responsibilities. By contrast the Soviet organization in Egypt seemed straightforward, with Dr Fazyl Kokanbaev, Commercial Counsellor at the Soviet Embassy, representing the Technobrom Export Organization, tough, stocky Ivan Vassilievitch Komzin, builder of the Kubyshev Dam on the Volga, as chief technical expert, and Georg Rafchinko as chief engineer at the site; but there was a bureaucratic shadow over all their work. They had to refer every major problem to the design engineers in Russia and this inevitably caused delays. The final designs for the first stage of construction did not reach Cairo until eight months after President Nasser had inaugurated the work, and the final designs for the entire dam were not complete and approved until the autumn of 1963.

The Russians and Egyptians, blaming each other for the slow progress, had enough to argue about without political disputes, and in the end, Mr Krushchev brought diplomatic discord to an end with some soothing words. This was plain common sense as far as the dam was concerned, because both countries had too much money and reputation at stake to risk failure over an enterprise too big to escape the attention of the world. For the Russians it was the greatest single symbol of Soviet technology and capacity to aid developing countries; for Egypt it was the symbol of revolutionary progress, one of the first and greatest of its creative decisions.

The sense of crisis generated by the lagging schedule therefore compelled both Russians and Egyptians at last to seek new and drastic ways to speed the work. They began by forming a joint Russo-Egyptian Committee to calculate the requirements in engineers and mechanics and to organize once again an adequate training programme. In August the governments signed two contracts involving expenditure of over £E18 million, of which £E5 million was for more Soviet equipment and just under £E4·5 million covered salaries for another 500 Soviet specialists.

At about this time a new and dynamic force began to make its mark on the enterprise. The application for tenders to undertake the excavation and filling work which had been published a year earlier had produced two offers, one from a consortium of twelve Egyptian contracting firms and another from the General Enterprises Engineering Company, which is still commonly known in Egypt as the company of Osman Ahmed Osman, the engineer who formed it with his brother, the late engineer Mohammed Osman, in 1950. Engineer Osman got the contract for the excavations. A smaller contract for concreting the tunnels, the hydro-electric station and the rock faces was given to a subsidiary of the powerful Misr group. The value of these two contracts was £E16 million but was later raised by £E4 million, largely to cover the cost of increasing the speed of the work. The contractors were given a down payment of £E2 million immediately on signing the agreement at the end of March, began work on May 1, and by August already had 2,000 labourers of their own at the site.

The Osman Company was the largest and most experienced engineering contracting firm in the country.[1] It had widened the Suez Canal, enlarged and improved Port Said harbour, built the coking plant at Helwan and was building the new international airport on the outskirts of Cairo, and it had executed many big projects in Kuwait, Saudi Arabia and Libya. Although this wealth of experience stood the firm in good stead in competing for the contract, the High Dam was nevertheless

[1] The Osman firm became part of the nationalized organization known as the Egyptian General Establishment for Enterprises and Construction, but it retained 50 per cent private capital and autonomy in operation. In 1964 the firm was denationalized for all overseas contracts and became known as Arab Contractors (Osman Ahmed Osman) Ltd.

a supreme challenge both in the financial risk involved and the national prestige at stake. Osman Ahmed Osman admits that 'he wanted to be part of the great project, to have his place in history with it'. Nevertheless he approached the financial risk with caution by sending two separate parties, unknown to each other, to formulate the estimates, while he and one or two of his closest associates made a third calculation of costs. The three estimates varied by only two per cent and, after allowing for a profit of half a million Egyptian pounds, were £E12 million less than the estimate submitted by the consortium. It was a margin so great that some time elapsed before the Supreme Committee for the dam could believe that a mistake had not been made[1].

Osman's contract for the High Dam was held in the name of a company called Arab Contractors Limited but it had the facilities of the entire Osman organization at its disposal. These included a department already with experience in assembling labour for big contracting jobs, which was an important part of the preparatory work. The department established recruiting offices in various parts of the country and offered high wages to the right kind of worker, with the result that the firm was recruiting workers at the rate of about 1,000 a month before the year was out. At the same time an all-out effort was mounted to provide the houses and the amenities that the workers would require at the desolate site. The effect on the work was not immediately remarkable but the morale of the workers began to mount visibly as truck-load after truck-load of labourers arrived, chanting the new song, 'Binebeyn el-sadd el-aali' – 'We are building the High Dam'.

Neither enthusiasm nor excitement were enough, however, to change a deeply critical situation. There was at the time about £E4 million worth of Soviet equipment at the site, including the first instalments of the main machines, such as the Ulanshev excavators, the 25-ton Zis dump trucks and the powerful Soviet rock drills, but Chief Engineer Amin el-Sherif who directed the work of the Arab Contractors quickly formed the opinion that the equipment was inadequate in both quantity and perform-

[1] In giving these facts to the author at the end of 1963, Engineer Osman said the estimates had proved correct.

ance. He said that his firm's contract could not be fulfilled unless more and efficient equipment were quickly brought into action. This was not a matter of guesswork, for Osman had trained assistants standing by the Russian machines for days on end calculating the work output and they reported that, overall, the Russian machines were 23 per cent less efficient than the equipment the company normally used. The powerful Ulanshev diggers emerged well from the test, but the dump trucks on which the Osman operation depended for moving millions of cubic yards of rock, had less than 77 per cent efficiency.

Pointing out that the dam was not going to be completed on time under these conditions, Osman Ahmed Osman decided that he must have some British dump trucks that he knew to have a much greater work capacity than the Russian vehicles. He was not concerned with the political climate; he was simply determined that he was not going to lose money and reputation on the biggest construction scheme in the whole of Egyptian history. His view, which had the full support of men like Ibrahim Zaki and Ahmed Said, those veterans of Nile dam engineering, met with great resistance from the Russians, and to overcome the opposition he pretended that they were needed for other work and would only be used temporarily at Aswan.

The facts were all in Osman's favour in this argument. Of the 14 million cubic yards of rock to be excavated there were still nearly 13 million to move when he took over the work, and all this rock had to be excavated, moved to dump areas and then retransported to the river for rock-filling at the coffer dams, before the summer of 1964. At this early stage the entire timetable of construction hinged on the excavations. The multiple operations required to complete the diversion channel, the tunnels and the coffer dams, could only proceed as fast as the excavators reached the required levels; it was impossible, for example, to reinforce tunnels until the tunnels were dug, or to rock-fill at the coffer dams until the rock was available. Osman had not only signed a contract of work but had entered himself under handicap in a race against time.

In retrospect it can be seen that the summer of 1961 was a turning-point, even if only in the recognition of manifest deficiencies and the exertion of will to overcome them. The engineers later admitted that inefficiency continued well into 1962, but even the failures imposed some logic on events. Because the work moved more slowly than expected, the supply lines began to keep pace with the work, and as the people working on the supply line all the way from Moscow to Aswan learnt by experience how to keep the supplies flowing to the site, stock-piling at last became possible. A base storage area, several square miles in extent and lying just north of the site, began slowly to fill with machines and equipment, and the spares needed for a broken machine were more and more often found ready to hand. There were 32,000 tons of Soviet equipment at the site in December.

There were then 9,000 Egyptian workers, that is, 3,000 more than were envisaged as needed for certain peak points of construction, and the number of Soviet engineers and technicians rose from 96 in April to 268 at the end of the year. Whereas only 300 tons of explosive had been used on the granite up to midsummer of 1961, 1,000 tons were detonated in the last six months of the year. Just over 400,000 cubic yards of rock were excavated in December. The building of the workshops and other surface installations, which Komzin had described as the core of the immediate problem, was going ahead with increasing speed. A temporary Nile harbour was completed and became an extra supply route in the autumn of the year.

All this was still more promise than fulfilment and it was not enough to dispel the sense of crisis in the minds of the Egyptian and Russian principals. With only half the target of 6·5 million cubic yards of rock excavated at the end of the year, the December rate of excavation was still far short of the rate needed if the 1964 deadline was to be kept. The site itself stood as witness to the immensity of the work not yet done. The top of the plateau had been levelled and the Ulanshev diggers, of which there were now seven at Aswan, were digging into it at several points and beginning to drive the shaft of the transport tunnel, but the whole operation still had a meaningless, haphazard appearance and there were engineers there who found it hard to believe that they could ever make up for lost time. Only thirty months remained for the completion of the first stage; thirty months in which the plateau must be split by a great chasm to take the

Nile, the tunnels bored and their gates built and hung, the hydro-electric station constructed, and the coffer dams built. In public it was maintained that work was going according to plan but there were experts who expressed their private opinion that the first stage could not be completed on time.

CHAPTER NINE

1962—The Turning Point

The anniversary celebrations of 1962 were, as usual, made the occasion for public demonstrations of confidence and to proclaim the close and cordial relations between the Russians and the Egyptians. The central feature of the celebrations on January 9 was the somewhat premature laying of the foundation stone of the hydro-electric works by President Nasser himself and his annual dam speech was this time devoted to countering the rumours of dissension and inefficiency. The dam, he declared, was a symbol of the friendship of Russians and Egyptians, whose co-operation was complete and cordial. And what was this talk about Soviet equipment? It was, he insisted, capable of all tasks. Nikita Krushchev himself sent a message to President Nasser which was duly published in *Al-Ahram* on January 21, in which he said 'We have no doubt that the first stage of the High Dam will be completed in 1964', and President Nasser replied that although the imperialists thought they could monopolize the undertaking of big projects, 'fortunately the technological advance of the Soviet Union has reduced this monopoly and imagination of the imperialists to illusion and self-deception'.

Nevertheless, the messenger who brought Mr Krushchev's letter was no less than Mr Ignat Novikov, Soviet Minister of Power Stations, whose purpose was to discover means to overcome the crisis in construction. At a Press conference he said that the 4 million cubic yards of rock excavated in 1961 was more than had been moved at any hydro-electric construction site in the world but he was either misled or misleading in exaggerating the figures by more than a million cubic yards. He did warn, however, that 1962 was going to be a decisive year and that the engineers 'expected to meet difficulties'. He toured the site once again with an anxious Dr Musa Arafa and his engineers and then returned to Moscow. The effect of this visit was not immediately seen, but it was to have decisive results before the year was out.

The High Dam entered its third construction year with the base area looking like a gold rush town springing to life on a far frontier. Buildings were going up everywhere: the smaller ones with untidy wooden frames and struts which, although intended for stone and concrete, seemed to be waiting for boards, a few nails and a hammer, and the larger ones, the sheds and workshops, with metal spars gleaming in the sunshine. About 6,000 rooms had been built for the workers in long, single-storey blocks and the contractors had thrown up temporary buildings which were an improvement on the tents and huts that workers had improvised for themselves. There were even luxuries that many of the inhabitants of this new town had never before enjoyed, such as air conditioning, piped water supplies, electric lighting and even deliveries of ice from an ice plant. Altogether the Government had spent nearly £E3 million pounds on the internal services, but the conditions were still far from perfect for everyone. Tents and huts were still scattered among the rocks around the base, giving it the air of a squatters' camp on the fringe of a frontier boom town. One still came across a group of men cooking their communal sheep over an open fire and the leather water-sack sweating in the heat. It was a man's town. Each day more men crowded into its untidy streets and added more bustle to the scene, and truck-loads of men would disappear into the desert as though bound for their 'diggings'; as indeed they were bound for one of the biggest diggings the world had ever seen, with the waters of the Nile as the rich reward to come.

The town was a reality by April. It straggled untidily over the granite plateau and reached out to the construction site itself. The mechanical repair shops and car maintenance sheds with their yards covered twelve acres of ground and, stocked with 800 machines, were able to employ about 350 men for an eight-hour shift every day of the year. The water towers of the air compressor station and the filtration plant rose aggressively against the landscape like stubby factory chimneys, competing for the skyline with the 15-ton overhead crane. The workshop for dressing chisels of the drilling machines and the concrete plants, for crushing, filtering and batching, were close to the working area and on the river itself there was a floating pumping station. The stores were in the base or at the other side, north of it, and held by this time great quantities of fuel, lubricants, materials of all kinds, and machinery and other equipment. One workshop at the northern end handled about seven tons of steel every shift for concrete reinforcement work and there was another steel assembly yard which would eventually have the task of assembling the big steel gates for the dam. In short, a small industrial town had come into existence for the sole purpose of building the dam, and seen like this, in quantity and variety, the requirements of the task reinforced the conception of its immensity. It was not just that they had to split open the granite plateau but, as they did so, to blend all these materials into the structures which would together form the dam.

The completion of the base at last was real progress, and there were now 10,000 labourers, with 115 Egyptian and 450 Russian engineers working with 11 Ulanshev excavators and 100 25-ton dump trucks at the site.[1] The rate of excavation was increasing but, as Mr Novikov and Engineer Musa Arafa knew, it was not increasing fast enough to overtake the work schedule. The machines and men were moving 15,000 cubic yards of rock a day and were doing their utmost to achieve a rate of 18,000, but the best working months of the year were already over and ahead lay the months of intense heat which the labourers from Northern Egypt found each day more difficult to endure. The first excitement of the enterprise was wearing thin among these men, whose simple minds saw no end to the hardship. Would the dam ever be built, they asked themselves as they looked around at the scene which seemed to them to be utter chaos? *Insha'allah* – if God wills. This mood of resignation, lacking the inspiration of their first faith, made their lot harder to bear, and

[1] The official, statistical report of the build-up at the site was given in an internal report of the High Dam authority as follows: 11 electrical excavators, 100 25-ton dump trucks, 4 1.25 cu.m. electrical shovels, 13 1.25 cu.m. diesel shovels, 36 bulldozers, 107 5- and 3.5-ton dump trucks, 200 lorries and other cars, 125 boring rigs of various sizes and types, 40 cranes of varying load capacities, 4 concrete mixers, 200 pumps of different discharges and lifting capacities, 4 electric transformer stations; total weight of this equipment 17,000 tons. About 23,000 tons of imported materials from the U.S.S.R. costing £E9 million F.O.B. were at the site.

the murmurs of discontent began to disturb the work at the very moment that new and greater efforts were being demanded of everyone.

The discontent exploded in sporadic disorders and strikes at the dam in the spring and it was decided that N.C.O.s of the army would move in as gang leaders. President Nasser was already by this time coming to the conclusion that he must make more radical changes in the organization of the work and the request for the army by Musa Arafa, who by this time was Minister of the High Dam, only strengthened his conviction. The top flight of Russian and Egyptian engineers were getting along worse instead of better. Mr Komzin, whose temper had been frayed by the interminable difficulties of the first two years, was rendered more unhappy and less inclined to patience by the death of his wife. Some of the experienced Egyptian engineers were saying openly that the Russian engineers were not of the same calibre as those from the West they had worked with in the past and did not know their job.[1] Probably by agreement, the two Governments decided to make a change at the top as had been tentatively envisaged when Novikov was in Cairo. In July, Mr Komzin was recalled to Russia and replaced by Aleksandro Aleksandrov and shortly afterwards Mousa Arafa was transferred to the High Dam Supreme Committee and his place as Minister was taken by Engineer Sidki Suleiman, an army officer in his forties.

Sidki Suleiman had qualified as a civil engineer before joining the army and many of the engineers working on the dam had gone through university with him. He had a distinguished army career, rising to the rank of Brigadier, and after the revolution he was attached to the National Production Council. This was at the time the central planning authority. It had given priority to the construction of the Aswan hydro-electric station, at which Ibrahim Zaki, the chief engineer at the dam, had been responsible for the civil engineering work. Suleiman had the reputation of being a 'go-getter', who would impart a new drive

[1] Engineer Ahmed Said: 'Compared with Western professionals they (the Russians) are amateurs'.

Eng. Ibrahim Kenawi: 'The Russians simply didn't know how to do the job here'. *Time*, October 19, 1962.

to the whole dam operation, just as Mahmoud Younis had saved the Suez Canal operations in 1956 and maintained them ever since with great success. The comparison with Younis was frequently made in 1962 to explain the appointment. Above all, Suleiman came to office at the command of President Nasser himself and with greater individual authority than any single man had formerly enjoyed at the dam. The superstructure of committees remained but was relegated to an advisory role; the Minister was now unquestionably 'the boss'. One of his first acts was to transfer his office from Cairo to the new administrative block which had been built to overlook the construction work from the west bank of the Nile, so that the organization was reversed, with the Ministry effectively at the site and the base administration in Cairo. He was in constant touch with his engineers and the contractors and he could act speedily to overcome their difficulties, phoning if necessary directly to the President himself. He only returned to Cairo for short periods at a time when problems needed his attention there; at other times he worked twelve or fourteen hours a day in his office or at the site and his tall, heavy figure topped with a topee, became as familiar at the diversion canal or in the tunnels as that of any of the working engineers. The change was of more than psychological importance, for it freed the work from a great deal of theoretical discussion in Cairo and established beyond any doubt the pre-eminence of the engineers at Aswan.

Aleksandrov was equally concerned to cut the red tape that had tied Komzin's hands. He took one look at the problems at Aswan and rushed back to Moscow for more men and equipment. He confessed to a Press conference in Cairo that he still had to refer any difficulties to Moscow for confirmation of the action he proposed to take, but he was obviously convinced that faster decision must be the prelude to faster action. The most important thing, he said, was to consult with the Egyptian engineers about the equipment needed and then get it to the site as quickly as possible. It was not a profound remark but at the time it had an inspiring effect on the Egyptians.

President Nasser had already over-ruled the Soviet objection to the use of non-Russian equipment by permitting the Ministry to order $840,000 worth of compressors and light rubber-tired rock drills from the Atlas Copco Company of Sweden with Swedish engineers to supervise them. The Soviet drills were reckoned by the engineers to be obsolete by Western standards and inefficient in some parts of the work on the Aswan granite. He also agreed that Osman Ahmed Osman could order on his own account twenty 35-ton dump trucks with Rolls Royce engines from the British firm of Aveling-Barford and these proved so efficient in action that the Ministry bought another twenty at its own expense. These orders, minuscule in comparison with the £E33 million so far spent on the dam, were part of the crisis and there is little doubt that the Egyptians would gladly have had more foreign equipment if they had had the money for it. Eventually two British excavators from the firm of Rustom-Bucyrus were used to lift the sand at Shellal and late in 1963 the U.A.R. Government begged Aveling-Barford to give them extraordinary priority by allowing more dump trucks, then at sea and bound for another destination, to be diverted to Egypt. At the climax of work before the first stage ended there were fifty-four of these trucks doing more dumping than 200 from Russia. A British expert from Dunlop was brought in when Dunlop tyres were ordered for the heavy vehicles, and on his suggestion gangs of workmen were set to work on the improvised roads to chip away the razor-like protruding edges of granite which were ripping the tyres to pieces.

The momentum for this gigantic operation was at last being reached, as though a giant wheel, having been pushed round by hand for a long time, had begun to spin on its own with increasing speed. The heat of the day was devoted mainly to maintenance work and laying the explosive charges in the holes drilled ready in the area of excavations. In the early afternoon the Soviet expert in charge would check the fuses, signal by siren that any worker who for any reason was in the vicinity was to remove himself and his truck and equipment, and at three o'clock about 20 tons of dynamite would explode in twelve boreholes, the reverberations of which could be felt as far away as Aswan town and heard much farther.

Each evening was like the next. The afternoon fades sharply in scarlet behind the hills of the other bank of the river, taking with it the heavy, bludgeoning heat of the day and drawing after it the first refreshing breeze to herald the evening. For a moment the desert seems cool. Then an army of men converge on the plateau by truck and spread themselves across the face of it like platoons taking position for battle, and suddenly, with the swiftness of the last fall of dark, the scene lights up with spectacular effect on man's latest and greatest endeavour on the Nile. Arc lights sharply throw a shining pool into the immensity of the night; thin strands of silvered beads trail away towards the glow of Aswan town; the headlights of cars and trucks in the distance flit like tipsy fireflies; the lights of the township prickle in the desert near by.

The work on the dam which has been numbed by the heat of the day now gets under way to the orchestrated sounds of men and machines. The main work on the rock at the diversion channel expresses itself in a ballet of grotesque shadows. The electric shovels nuzzle their long snouts into the debris and the fire of their conflict with the rock pours in blue flame from the jaws; trucks groan with granite loads up improvised escarpments and men looking no bigger than insects crawl about everywhere.

The contrast with the recent past was already striking. Two years earlier such a night would have been empty of sight or sound, except perhaps for the timid intrusion of a boat on the Nile or the lonely light from the window of the laboratory on the west bank. Even a year earlier President Nasser's monument perched high above the river looked out on little visible results for months of work and the total effort mobilized in the debris of geological ages appeared totally inadequate to the task. In the executive offices among the blueprints, estimates and work schedules the anxieties were still unrelieved but on the ground the transformation was beginning to take place. It was possible from the laboratory to look across the river and *see* what was happening, for the line of the channel from the downstream entrance past the tunnelled section to Khor Kundi was at last visible.

The plateau was broken by a series of monstrous cavities which, one could see, were blending together as the work proceeded. At the downstream side the diversion had already the shape of a deep valley but it was still being excavated at different levels and a natural block of rock stood across the mouth to keep the river from the workings. Roads improvized on temporary escarpments at the levels of work led only to the excavators, which chewed and groaned and sometimes screamed as they bit into the granite left loose by the day's dynamiting. The excavators filled a 25-ton truck in anything from a minute and a half to two minutes and a half and moved 130 cubic yards of rock an hour. The art of the excavating was to ensure that a truck was always waiting while another was filling so that the flow of rock from the site never paused. Each digger had its line of trucks, the empty ones rattling and bumping up the escarpment and the loaded ones screaming in low gear as they crawled down past them, often edging hazardously close to the rough-cut edge of the road and the 'drop' into the valley below.

On the upstream side of the channel, where they had started from the natural depression in the plateau running from Khor Kundi, the digging levels were lower than downstream and shelved steeply from the entrance to the 200-feet rock face of the central section, where bays cut into the face already marked the proposed inlets of the tunnels. This work was protected by a sand coffer dam 65 feet high and 270 yards long, which had been constructed in a month by sluicing over 300,000 cubic yards of sand through pipes on the west bank, the method that the Russian engineers intended to use for the upstream coffer of the main dam. It was the first time this method had been used on the Nile and was on a small scale but it demonstrated the solidity that could be achieved. It was firm enough to serve as a road even for heavily laden trucks going round the excavations and for as long as it was left in position it served as one of the main highways at the site.

Meanwhile, men were hard at work in the belly of the plateau cutting the tunnels. A tubular subterranean 'highway', 650 yards long and 25 yards wide had been bored from its starting-point near the river-side on a gentle gradient until it bisected the line of the tunnels and as each in turn was reached excavation of that tunnel started immediately in both the upstream and the downstream directions. About half the tunnel excavation had been done. Work was proceeding on four tunnels by digging out the top half of the tunnel-cylinder, leaving the bottom half of the cylinder as a temporary road for the trucks and a rock floor for the mobile drilling and concreting platforms. The difficult part of this operation was breaking into the virgin granite; the removal of the lower half of the tunnels was a normal and relatively simple job which, when the time came, proceeded at great speed. The dump trucks moved freely in both directions in and out of the workings.

Not a moment was now being wasted. As each section was excavated the teams moved in to reinforce the rock; first, the Soviet drilling teams to bore and fit the steel rods; then the placing of the seven-ton steel frames which had been erected sectionally above ground and were welded together below ground to fit the semi-cylindrical roof; and, finally, the concrete was moulded on these frames to a thickness of one yard.

As this work spread underground, the heart of the plateau acquired a nightmarish quality of light, shade and noise: the harsh glare of the floodlights and the dark brown caverns of shade, the intermittent, blinding blue light of the welding and drilling plants, dripping water and the myriad reflections on murky pools, grotesque shadows of men and machines, mud; the screech of the drills, and the throb and clank of trucks in the enclosed passages. Below ground just as much as in the channel outside the race with time was at last engaged in most spectacular fashion.

The autumn was in any case a crucial period of the year. The sluices of the old dam were then fully open allowing the lake behind it to fall to the lowest annual level for about four months and the engineers were under great pressure to complete in this short time all the works on the banks of the river and canal that were laid bare. Not much of the drilling, injecting and strengthening had been done in 1961, so that the autumn of 1962 was critical, and the autumn of 1963 would obviously be decisive.

Mr Ignat Novikov had said at the start of the year that 1962 would be vital and so it proved to be. Although it was clear that only supreme efforts on the grandest scale could re-establish the schedule of work for the diversion of the river in May of 1964, the engineers were at last confident that such an effort was in their power. The base area and installations were complete, machines were running more efficiently and were at least being

1 The first Aswan Dam as it was when completed in 1902

2 The first dam after the second heightening in 1933 and as it is today

3*a* Charges blasting the granite plateau for the excavation of the diversion channel

3*b* Making a slurry of sand, for the temporary blocks on the diversion channel

4*a* The upstream entrance of the diversion channel, showing the temporary sand coffer dam

4*b* Dredging clear the first sand coffer dam at the downstream exit of the channel

5*a* (*above*) Soviet excavators digging out the floor of a tunnel

5*b* (*right*) Three of the six tunnels nearing completion in 1963

6 The rock-fill upstream coffer dam nearing completion, May, 1964

7 *From left to right:* Osman Ahmed Osman, Prime Minister Aly Sabry, and Engineer Sidki Suleiman Minister of the High Dam, with Chief Engineer Ibrahim Zaki between Osman and the Prime Minister

8 Workers entraining at Aswan

9*a* Stones from the temples assembled on Elephantine Island

9*b* Dr W. Adams supervising the excavating of a Meroitic village

10*a* Façade of the Great Temple of Abu Simbel

10*b* A worker sitting on the foot of a statue of Ramses II at Abu Simbel

11 The inner court of the Great Temple of Abu Simbel

12 May 15, 1964: Dump trucks closing the gap in the upstream coffer dam

speedily repaired, the supplies of materials were flowing more freely to the site, there were 1,500 Russian specialists, 200 Egyptian engineers and 9,000 technicians and 12,000 Egyptian labourers at work. In the month of December the Arab Contractors excavated and dumped 550,000 cubic yards of the toughest granite in the world, which was about 130,000 more than either the Americans, the Russians or the Canadians had achieved by record-breaking efforts on their own grounds. 'We will divert the river on time,' said Chief Engineer Zaki at the end of the year; and the burly Ahmed Said took his pipe from his mouth to state emphatically, 'If not, I will cut my throat'.

Of the many men who laboured long and hard to achieve the triumph of December there was one who had borne an onerous and direct burden. Amin el-Sherif, chief engineer of the Arab Contractors, was responsible for the excavations which were far behind when he came to the dam and were the key to the entire operation at this stage. He worked day and night at the site for over a year, snatching what sleep he could in his office. He might have been separated from his family in Cairo by ten thousand miles for all he saw of them. Each day he reported the amount of rock moved to Osman Ahmed Osman by telephone and charted the steady increase in the level of excavation until in December he reported the record rate that foreshadowed the successful completion of the first stage on time. It was in these happy circumstances that Osman Ahmed Osman made one of his periodical visits to the site in December and as he toured the workings in a black Volkswagen car with Amin el-Sherif at the wheel he stopped from time to time to exchange a cheery word with the workers. 'Let's go, Amin', he said, after one of these stops; but there was no response and never could be again.

Amin el-Sherif, his task accomplished, was dead. He was fifty.

CHAPTER TEN

1963 – Year of Success

On the first of January, 1963, a large signboard was posted prominently overlooking the main entrance road to the site and smaller editions of it were to be found in many places, including the offices of the Minister, Sidki Suleiman, and Mr Aleksandrov. It proclaimed in Arabic and in Russian that only 500 working days were left and by implication it meant that the first crucial stage of construction would be completed and the diversion of the Nile would take place on May 15 1964. The target was set. Each dawn the figure was changed on every sign so that no one could forget the relentless passage of too little time.

Now for the engineers directing the work there was less rest than ever as the pace quickened and the operation became more complex. The Minister, Chief Engineer Zaki and Ahmed Said, Aleksandror and Radchinko, and many others, began their work at daybreak by touring the workings and the workshops and before the morning was out were back at their offices to confer, administer and command. Lunch was invariably late, the afternoon rest short, before the great dusk invasion of the labourers began and they returned to the site for the long evening of work, which was broken again only briefly for the evening meal. The fleshpots of the Cataract Hotel saw them less and less and Cairo saw them seldom, and Taha Abou Wafa, the efficient Under-Secretary of the Ministry at the equivalent of Army HQ – the Cairo offices of the Ministry – seemed to live at the end of the telephone. Faces were lined with fatigue, tempers sometimes frayed and anxiety was never far from the surface, but with the passage of the months confidence mounted, and with it the sense of achievement. Russian and Egyptian alike were proud men. Dmitri Zarkailishov, the 30-year-old explosives expert, who sent his wife home in 1960, extended his own stay well into 1963: 'Here you have a chance to work harder', he said, and meant it.

Engineer Gamal el-Batrawy had replaced Amin el-Sherif as

chief of the Arab Contractors' operations. He was one of the most trusted men of Osman Ahmed Osman, for whom he had already directed the enlargement of Port Said harbour and the widening of the Suez Canal, both of them big jobs by any standard. A man in his forties, of medium height, quiet in speech and dedicated, he made his office his home and never left the site for months on end, even to see his family in Cairo. His own staff of engineers rose to 100 and his labour force to 12,000, or double the total force at one time thought enough for the work.

The system of maintenance and repairs improved so much that the maintenance shift during the heat of the day was eliminated and a third working shift inserted. This meant that the labour continued unbroken during the twenty-four hours and the workers on the daytime shift endured the appalling heat of Aswan region, which even those who were acclimatized found hard to bear. 'Surprisingly few collapsed with heat exhaustion,' said one of the engineers, but how many is not known.

Despite the added hardship work continued without any repetition of the labour troubles of 1962. This was not simply due to the presence of army 'gangers' in charge of the labour. The morale and the material conditions had improved so much that work even in the most trying circumstances was accepted willingly. The contracting firms provided houses for their workers, either at the site for single men or on the outskirts of Aswan for the married men, and in addition they provided recreational clubs where they could freely enjoy more entertainment than they had ever been accustomed to. The Arab Contractors' club, for example, had a swimming-pool, a cinema, television, a games room, a library, a restaurant and a non-alcoholic bar. (Alcohol was not allowed anywhere at the site.) Pay was high enough to attract workers and render unnecessary the 1962 system, bordering on conscription, whereby the workless or those who were redundant elsewhere, were given little chance to refuse a call to the dam. Now the poorest worker was getting about £E10 a month plus free accommodation, food and recreation and there were many who were drawing about £E30 in cash. The effect was felt in Cairo where it became steadily more difficult to get domestic servants, a facility for which Cairo was formerly renowned. By the end of the year there were no less than 30,000 workers at the dam, five times the maximum originally envisaged.

Above all there was the feeling of achievement. It reached down to the most ignorant workers, who felt that *they* were the dam builders, and among the more educated men was reflected in a sense of mission. Many of them became more and more excited as each day made visible the immense dimensions of the undertaking and to these people neither comforts nor hardships seemed of much account. They would, one felt, boast to sons and grandsons of their part in building the dam. Two Englishmen who were teasing a bus driver in not too kindly fashion about some tiresome speech-making at the dam were silenced when he turned on them to say, quietly and with dignity, in English, 'I am a simple Egyptian. I thought we could never build this big dam and now we are doing it. It doesn't matter to me if there's some *qalam fadi*'.[1]

Spurred by propaganda and persuasion, hundreds of university youths volunteered to work at the dam during their 1963 vacations for a wage of £E15 a month and were praised by the engineers for their enthusiasm. Their efforts were probably more valuable to public morale than in actual work at the site, but many of them returned to Aswan when they finished school in order to take training courses.

Kamel Shenouda of the laboratory was typical of the Egyptians with a sense of mission. He was reared and educated in the sophisticated atmosphere of pre-revolutionary Alexandria but he spent so much time in Nubia after leaving the university that the Nubians considered him an honorary citizen of their frontier world. Seven of those years were spent in resettling Nubians and designing projects for villages and land reclamation as belated rehabilitation of peasants displaced by the second heightening of the old dam in the thirties. When this work was finished he spent three years in Alexandria before receiving once again a call to Nubia, this time to work for the High Dam which would eventually destroy beneath its lake every house, field and tree of his creation.

Shenouda worked at the laboratory from its beginning, long before the dam itself became a practical proposition and always

[1] Empty words.

in conditions prosaic enough to destroy by their habitual commonplace all feelings of adventure. He rose to be chief of a triumvirate of three who shared a small box-like room and he spent almost all his working hours for many years in it. Pinned to the walls behind and at the side of his desk were coloured diagrams of the structure of the river-bed, one of which was a cross-section in depth compiled from the borings of French and German specialists, and another showing a cross-section compiled later by the Egyptians themselves on the line of the dam selected by the Russians. The years of sweaty discomfort were gone. His office was air-conditioned and he lived in an air-conditioned house in a small residential town built for engineers and officials among the craggy hills of the west bank and he could divert himself watching television which had been brought to Aswan for the workers at the dam and the Kima fertilizer factory. These small comforts counted for much in the scorched wilderness of Aswan and Shenouda recorded them with pleasure; but the earlier absence of them, the years spent in his barren office almost isolated from the physical creation of the dam, never destroyed his imaginative comprehension of his part, minuscule though it might be, in the great, creative enterprise.

Womenfolk who had no active part in the work, and were cut off from their friends and pleasures, found Aswan harder to bear. Some wives never set up house at Aswan, or spent a great part of the year away from it. Those who lived there contributed to the effort by patiently enduring the boredom of long hours alone at home, enlivened only by evenings spent before the glassy eye of the television set, in order to tend their husbands. According to Shenouda his wife did not complain, but he married after he began to work at the dam and, as he said, she knew then where her home for the next few years would be.

Most of the Russians, both men and their families living in air-conditioned Kima flats with their own social club provided by the Egyptian Government at their doorstep, seemed perfectly content at Aswan. The punishment for any serious mistake at work or social offence outside work was a one-way ticket to Russia, and strong men were known to shed tears of regret when it was inflicted on them. Yet there seemed little to commend their Aswan existence. It was confined to their own relatively small community and consisted of gossiping over a Russian meal or in the shade of their houses, having a few vodkas, watching a Russian film or playing a game of table tennis at the club. They were still rarely to be seen enjoying the modest high life of the Cataract Hotel or the middling life of the Grand, or sailing in the moonlight on the Nile.[1] Perhaps the domestic conditions were better than any enjoyed at home and counted greatly with them, for their flats were new, air-conditioned, and were big enough to house their families in comfort and to entertain their friends. Whatever the reason, life in the Kima industrial suburb on the edge of the tropics suited them.

Once a year the Russians threw a party for their Egyptian colleagues but that was almost the limit of international merry-making. There was still little mixing out of working hours. Nevertheless, relations between the Egyptians and the Russians had improved greatly during 1963, particularly among the engineers who had shared the anxiety of preceding years and now shared the imminent prospect of success. The work schedule climbed steadily to the desired level, giving less cause for recrimination and more chance to recognize merit. The seed of improvement had been sown by Aleksandrov in 1962 when he quickened the supply of materials, machinery and men. Within a fortnight in November he brought in 200 more Soviet experts and ordered an extra 11,000 tons of needed equipment. The Egyptians, for their part, at last recognized the need for an uninhibited training programme and the agreement was revised in December, so that teachers, equipment and films sufficient to train 500 technicians arrived from Moscow shortly after the turn

[1] Four young English specialists who advised on the use and maintenance of their firms' equipment at the dam, lived gregariously and happily at the Cataract Hotel. They were not always the same four, but at the end of 1963 they were Peter Fraser, of Dunlop Rubber Company's overseas division, Arthur Cawthorne, of Aveling-Barford, Grantham, Clive Wooley, of Rolls Royce, and Frank Stephenson, of Rustom-Bucyrus. I first met them installing a massive safe in the New Cataract Hotel, using balks of timber and ropes, a task for which they volunteered when the frantic hotel manager found no one able to move the safe from his hall where it had been dumped unceremoniously. Each day they went to the site like any of the engineers or technicians, playing their small but useful parts in the enterprise, but their presence was never mentioned in the Egyptian Press. No doubt it was thought undesirable to report that non-Russian machines were at work. In contrast with the Russians, they were on good and gossiping terms with the Egyptians.

of the year. Batches of Egyptians were sent to Russia to be prepared for work on the hydro-electric station.

Osman's workers excavated 654,000 cubic yards of rock and sand in July of 1963 and by that time were passing the work peak in the open channels. The last rock on the downstream side, a small outcrop near the tunnel outlets on the western edge of the channel, was dug out on November 23 and this left only 157,000 cubic yards for removal from the upstream section, a matter of ten days' work at the speed achieved, which was being left in position as a ramp-road to the tunnel entrances. By this time most of the digging was taking place in the tunnels, which were being excavated to their bed level, reinforced and concreted section by section at a greatly increased speed to achieve a target date for completion early in 1964. The great explosions which in 1962 had reached a maximum of 26 tons at one time, no longer sent shudders through the plateau; the neat, precisely-placed charges were now measured in kilograms.

There were 34,000 men working at the dam. The Arab Contractors had excavated their 13 million cubic yards of granite by the end of the year and with 135 working days to Diversion-Day the concrete company was now under pressure. This was a penalty of the early delays, without which the Misr company would have been able to concrete in sequence, stage by stage as each was completed. The *blitz* of the preceding eighteen months had brought the work of various sections to a climax, and this compelled Misr to concrete the sections simultaneously. The big batching plant built at the site was capable of producing all the 24,000 cubic yards of concrete needed but another and smaller plant was erected and came into service in November 1963 to make sure that the daily output would be equal to the extraordinary demands that the closing stage created.

Work began on the housing of the hydro-electric station at the downstream side of the tunnels in August and three months later the Arab Contractors began dumping over 5 million cubic yards of rock for the main upstream coffer dam. These works heralded the last phase of the first stage of the work on the High Dam, and, bearing in mind that the coffer would be moulded into the main structure, the engineers could say that they had begun to build the dam itself.

Work on the upstream coffer dam should have begun in the autumn of 1962 when the lake behind the old dam was low, but because the work on the diversion was behind schedule, the start was delayed until the autumn of 1963. The Russians pumped the sand through pipes into the river, a method which the international consultants had regarded with great caution, for the coffer dam was being built in the reservoir of the old dam, where the depth of water exceeded 115 feet and the flow of the river reached 400,000 cubic feet a second, conditions which had never been faced before in the use of the sand-sluicing system. The Russians, however, had used it in damming the Dnieper for the Dneprodzershinsk hydro-electric station and Dr Musa Arafa and a group of Egyptian engineers had been impressed by both its cheapness and speed when they saw it in use there. It had also been tested on a small scale in building the coffer dams in the diversion channel. By the autumn of 1963 the sluicing method was, in any case, essential to the schedule, for without it the main coffer dam could not have been completed before the following May.

The method could be seen in spectacular fashion on the west bank, where water was pumped through massive hoses into a sand basin in the natural dunes to make slurry, which was then sucked through pipes to the site of the coffer dam in the river. The sand from Shellal, which was too far away for pumping, was loaded by two British-built Rustom-Bucyrus excavators onto trains using the newly extended track. Fourteen trains a day carrying fifty tons of sand in twenty trucks formed an artificial dune at the northern end of the work side on the east bank, and the sand was soaked at the foot of the dune and then pumped to its position in the river. Once in the river, the sand was consolidated by giant vibrating columns.

By the end of the year, the river was being narrowed from both banks but the coffer dam was under water. Engineer Batrawy's men were loading rock from prepared dumping areas onto trucks which deposited it onto large vibrating shoots and sieves on the river-side that separated the rock mechanically into different sizes as it slid into barges. The barges then dumped the rock into the river at sites marked out by buoys.

The grand design was at last apparent to the observer. As the coffer dams were built in the river, the diversion channel and its tunnels were progressively cleaned behind the temporary coffer dams at each end. The natural block at the downstream side of the channel had long since been removed and sand dams were holding back the river in the channel, awaiting their destruction on the great day of the river diversion.

Powerful concrete buttresses separated and defended the entrances to the six tunnels, which were being shaped to take the control-gates. These, among the biggest ever constructed, were already in Egypt and being moved in sections from Alexandria to Aswan for assembling at the site. At the exits of the tunnels, the housing of the hydro-electric station was well advanced on its heavy reinforced concrete platform and was being made ready for assembling the turbines.

At the upstream end of the tunnels, there were new inlets to be seen above the level of the westernmost two of the six entrances already excavated, and from these inlets new tunnels were being dug on an incline to join those immediately below them. Eventually the remaining four tunnels would have similar entrances at a higher level. The lower routes on the upstream side were intended to provide channels for the river during the first four years when the reservoir was filling but would be useless when storage passed the level required only for the storage of silt because they would provide access only to 'dead' water. They would then be blocked with concrete, so that the 'live' water above could gain access to the turbines from the upper inlets. Similarly, the gates were being slotted at the lower tunnels and would in due course be raised into new concrete grooves in time for the flow of water at the higher and permanent levels. The top tunnels were in reality part of the second stage of building, and it was evidence of the progress made by the end of 1963 that work had begun on them.

At this point it was beyond question that success was in sight, despite the miscalculations and maladministration, and the inevitable delays they caused during the first years of work. It was a supreme tribute to the Russians and the Egyptians in the final count that the immense difficulties had been overcome so far without any major calamity overtaking them. There had been one extremely dangerous moment when the sand in the coffer dam began to slip, a process which, had it been detected too late or allowed to continue, would have destroyed a great part of the work already done and made the target date impossible of achievement, but all men and machines required to correct the defect had been mobilized in time. This critical occasion pointed to the one supreme test of all the work that had yet to be faced when the flood waters of 1964 rolled with all their strength against the upstream coffer dam – a testing time to which the international consultants had drawn attention in their first critical study of the German design – but the engineers, both Russian and Egyptian, were confident that the river would be held. The river did, in fact, eventually put this judgement to a severe test.

Many men have paid with their lives and no doubt many more will do so before the great dam itself stands in all its glory across the Nile. A rockfall from the cliff face at the outlet of the tunnels killed at least eleven men; six men were destroyed by explosive when the warning system failed to report that one charge had not detonated; some trucks navigating the hazardous roads on the escarpment tumbled into the valley. On one occasion the chutes on a barge dumping rock in the river were opened too soon and the Nubian standing on the rock was dropped with it. At the passionate demand of his fellow villagers all work was stopped on the river while divers hunted for his body as far away as the sluices of the old dam to which it might have been swept by the flow of the water, but it was never found. With thousands of unlettered men working with powerful machines in wild surroundings it was inevitable that such accidents should occur, but no authoritative figures of those killed, or those whose bodies broke under the strain of work in such harsh conditions, has ever been given. The Arab Contractors reckon about fifty men lost their lives each year, a figure which would not be surprising, but some say that it is too low. At least those who died lost their lives in a creative enterprise, far removed from the destruction of war, and the dam will stand as their monument even if neither granite pillar nor roll of honour commemorates their death 'on the field of honour'.

They had played their small part in bringing a great enterprise to the threshold of achievement in the fourth year of the work, for it had been said at the very beginning that the date of the diversion of the river would determine the date of completion. There could be, it is true, no slackening of effort in the early months of 1964, but the cleft plateau, its immense man-made chasm and its tunnels, even the sealed transport tunnel that at one time had pierced its heart, the structure of rock and sand rising steadily day by day beneath the waters of the Nile, stood witness to the day of triumph on May 15. The tourists of that winter no longer looked to white lines on the cliff, for, as their boats were directed through the narrowing channel in the river, they could see for themselves the valley which so soon would take the waters on which they sailed. Beneath their keels the giant dam was already taking shape.

PART THREE

The Doomed Land

CHAPTER ELEVEN

The Nubians

The banks of the Nile for 350 miles from Aswan to a point south of the Dal cataract in the Sudan is Nubia. The northern part, inside Egypt, is known as Lower Nubia and to the ancient Egyptians was Wawat; the region from Wadi Halfa southwards was part of the ancient land of Kush and to the Greeks and Romans was the northern reach of the corner of Africa which they called Ethiopia, the country of the burnt-faced people. It has always been a natural and visible frontier. The valley consists of harsh cliffs broken by plains of sand that roll down to the water's edge and the river flows roughly over its broken rocky bed until it breaches the first cataract at Aswan and begins its sober journey to the north. Its people stand apart. They have preserved from obscure beginnings spoken languages of their own and their dark skins herald the start of black Africa.

At some distant time there were peoples living in Africa who sowed the seeds of human pride, raising themselves above all other living things by acquiring skills, forming self-conscious societies and nurturing an embryonic spiritual sense. The combination of harsh land and a rough river made of Nubia a border march between these peoples. It was an inhospitable corridor over a great and uncharted range of time, whether at the beginning for earliest primitives moving north or, later, for civilized men in a two-way traffic in search of wealth or conquest; always the outcrop of desolation along the Nile between the first and third cataracts attenuated the thrusts.

Here the links between man and man were forged in relentless heat, stretched, and often broken by the strain. It barred the savages from the civilized; it made the civilized pause in their advance on the primitive. Links fashioned by black Africans, by Egyptians, Greeks and Romans have marked the Nubian reach with everything from squiggles on the rock to majestic temples, which make it a supreme textbook on ancient history, enabling us to understand a great deal about the meeting of men and minds at a frontier of the early world.

As civilization advanced in Europe and spread across the world, the inhospitable land was forgotten. The drifting sand shrouded through the centuries its many monuments leaving a ghostly greatness to hint at the past, like the colossal heads that an adventurous traveller found early last century protruding from a sea of sand to mark the site of Abu Simbel, the supreme monument of all. Diligent historians since that time have recovered and interpreted much of the past so that Nubia has become an immense open-air museum of relics spread upon the sand and with the sun to light it. The inhabitants lived their simple, almost unchanging lives in this curious environment on the banks of the river.

The High Dam has doomed for ever this land of Nubia, its monuments and the homes and farms of 100,000 people living in it. The whole Sudanese town of Wadi Halfa, the villages with their clean, whitewashed houses, the palm trees and the thin, struggling crops, the traditions and the penurious living of a hardy and proud people who have clung to the banks of the river from generation to generation, will all vanish in the reservoir.

There are references to Nubians in pharaonic times but whence and when they came is not yet clear even to scholars. Nor is it known exactly when their language began to be spoken on the Nile. An old Nubian language has been identified in inscriptions of the eighth century A.D., but as a written script it did not survive the conversion of the Christian Kingdom of Dongola in the fourteenth century, being replaced by Arabic as the Nubians were Islamized. Now there remain two spoken languages, one Kenuzi, used by people for about ninety miles along the river from Aswan, and the other Mahasi, which is used southwards to Dongola in the Sudan. These two languages are separated by about twenty-five miles of river-bank where Arabic is spoken by an intrusive people of bedouin and Sudanese origin. The speakers of Kenuzi and Mahasi cannot understand each other and the latter language has more in common with Danagla, the language of the Dongalawis.

Yet the cultural and ethnic link of the Nubians is complete

from Aswan to Dongola and the language division takes place not at the frontier but well inside Egypt. They have always stood apart from their compatriots in Egypt simply because they are regarded and regard themselves as separate, and in the Sudan because they are one more of the designated tribal and regional groups. Centuries ago the Moslem conquerors called them the Berbers and their region the Bilad el-Barabra, country of the Berbers. Even after their conversion to Islam they preserved a different way of life and for many centuries associated with the Egyptians as little as possible. Less than a century ago the Nubian women still went naked except for a small skirt of leather thongs while their Egyptian sisters, true to the traditions of the faith, were shrouded in black and showed the forearms and ankles in public only when they were compelled to do so for work in the fields. Not many years ago travellers and guidebooks described dislike for the Egyptians as a characteristic of the Nubians and there is no doubt that an already deep-rooted antagonism was reinforced at the beginning of last century when young men were dragged from the Nubian villages to swell the ranks of the army of Mohammed Aly the Great. It has been dissipated in recent years, and Nubian emigrants will now sometimes marry Egyptian wives in the towns and cities of lower Egypt, but it can well to the surface very easily. There has not been the same antagonism between the people of Upper Nubia and the adjoining Sudanese.

Travelling south on the Nile, the change to Nubia from the Egyptian area left behind is immediately apparent. The Egyptian villages, because they are built on valuable land at the river-side or in the delta, are congested and dirty, whereas the Nubians, who have much land but few fields, have built their villages on the rock and sand where they can have both space and cleanliness. The mud walls and houses are whitewashed and gaily decorated with inset colourful plates, saucers and tureen lids, and the doors, the interiors and the exteriors have bold and bright designs painted on them, some of which are formal and said to be ancient in origin, and others, such as the flower-pot motif which is found everywhere, obviously modern. Often the decorations inside the houses include pictures cut from illustrated magazines.

There never has been a railway between Shellal, just outside Aswan, and Wadi Halfa, so the villages of Nubia have always been compelled to depend for contact on the river or difficult river-side tracks. Those villages live together which have access to each other, having become in time large family or tribal groupings within which almost all the social life of the communities takes place. The great occasions are the celebrations of local saints' days, for each village has at least the tomb of one saint to venerate, and when each holy day arrives in turn the womenfolk of the associated villages gather the family belongings in a basket and march off to camp out for its duration. Contact with the world outside Nubia is slender, again depending on rough tracks or the weekly mail-boats which call at some of the villages and provide the postal service for them all. This relative isolation has encouraged the people to preserve old traditions, most of which may be lost to the social historian by the disappearance of the villages themselves.[1]

Nubia is rainless and has probably been unable to support its own population for a century. Even where crops can be grown on land watered by the river, the heat is so great that many of them have to be cut before ripening and used as fodder for animals. One might expect the people to be great fishermen, but they are not, and their methods of fishing and of agriculture are as primitive as they were in the times of the pharaohs. The region lives on the remittances brought by the mail-boats from the Nubian menfolk working, usually as domestic servants or *bawwabat*, hall porters, in the towns and cities of lower Egypt. Few of the Nubian villages have more than half their males at home, and most of those at home are old or very young: some villages have no adult men at all. This gives Nubia the unique characteristic of being inhabited by women, children and old men. The young exile usually returns home to marry a girl

[1] 'Nobody seems to have time to record such folk-art or the ways of its creators, yet the destruction of this living tradition is quite as tragic as the destruction of ancient monuments', wrote Jacquetta Hawkes in *The Observer* of February 26, 1961, after a journey up the Nile. A Nubian Ethnographical Survey was, in fact, launched that year by the Social Research Centre of the American University of Cairo at the instigation and direction of Dr Robert A. Fernea, an American anthropologist, and under the overall supervision of Dr Laila Shukry el-Hammamsy, the Egyptian director of the centre.

from his own village or community and when she is pregnant he goes back to his work in the town. A year, or two, or three, may elapse before he returns to see his wife again, or his child for the first time, and then it will be only briefly to see his parents and beget another child and depart. Many of them live most of their lives in this way and return finally in old age to buy, if possible, a bit of land on which to end their days at home. Inevitably some marry another woman in the town where they work, or as in some cases in recent times, they take their Nubian wives to the town, and in both cases the link with the home village becomes more tenuous as the years pass. The unnatural life of separation and the poverty that gives rise to it has, however, done little to wean the Nubians from affection for their river-side, and even though the future could offer them no more than the past, only a small proportion has willingly left it for ever.

The Egyptian Nubians have been driven from the river three times before, when the first Aswan Dam was built in 1902 and twice heightened later, forming the immense reservoir in which the High Dam is now being built. Each enlargement of the lake submerged more of their land, encouraging the migratory process to the Egyptian towns. Some moved as short a distance as possible to find work in Aswan, and the Government transplanted others in the sugar cane region of Kom Ombo; yet others just scrambled higher up the banks when they found some new land irrigated by the rise and fall of the river and, years later, the Government capitulated to their passionate insularity and designed new communities for them. In the late summer, autumn and winter, from the rising of the river to its decline, they live in a barren world, for all their land vanishes and they cling to their villages on the edge of the desert, with the foliage of the palm trees waving in the air just above the level of the river and all else gone.

The conditions of poverty and the system of migration to the towns applies also to the Nubians of the Sudan, although they were less affected by the heightening of the Aswan Dam. Some of them found work in Wadi Halfa and Khartoum. There were also about 5,000 Nubians from Egypt in Halfa, which stands apart from the general picture of abject poverty in the region. It lies just south of the Sudan border and, as capital of the province and the terminal link of the Khartoum railway and the Shellal passenger boats, it enjoys a small influx of wealth denied elsewhere in Nubia. It boasts a sizeable hotel, which stands in spacious river-side gardens where the Nile steamers moor at the end of their journey from Egypt, and its streets are wide and edged with low buildings in the cantonment style favoured by the British east of Suez.

When President Abboud agreed to accept $42 million compensation for Nubia, he doomed Wadi Halfa, its hotel and its streets and, even as I write, the waters are beginning to rise against the town and the villages all the way north to the High Dam. For the Nubians this is the end of their world, the last great migration without possibility of return, unless some hardy souls try to scratch a living on still higher shores of the lake.

The Sudanese were slow to accept the inevitability of this fate, stubbornly believing until very late that the dam would not be built or by some other miracle they would be reprieved. 'What now, Mohammed?' – 'All is with God'; and Mohammed would shrug and point to the sandy hill behind to suggest he would climb and build. 'But that hill will be under water, Mohammed!' – 'God is merciful'. In truth, Mohammed did not believe that his town would be left to crumble in the waters of his Nile and was inclined to say with many Halfawis as late as 1962, that flood or no flood, he would stay beside the river. He would humour the curious by talking about it, that was all.

Those Halfawis who did face up to the realities of the situation were easily recognized by their anger, and as this anger would clearly multiply as the truth was more and more recognized, the Sudan Government sought to pacify opinion in advance by forming a commission to determine where the Nubians would resettle and promising that they would not be forced to go anywhere against their will. This was a mistake, for everyone knew that they would choose to move as short a way as possible along the Nile, which meant, in terms of the potential sites, resettlement near Khartoum.

The Government had already plans to build a dam on the Atbara river, 800 miles south-east of Halfa, at a place called Khasm el-Girba, and from the Government's point of view this was a good chance to settle the land around the dam with trained farmers. Short of offering them a site away from any river, Khasm el-Girba was a place that the Nubians were least likely to choose for themselves, for it was not only far distant from the relatives who were in the towns of the Sudan and Egypt but was as different as it possibly could be from their homeland. The Atbara is a seasonal river, dry for part of the year and then stormy with flood water coursing down to the Nile, and the Khasm el-Girba region is assailed by violent tropical rains. They were used to storms on the Nile and strong winds but compared with the wild emptiness of the Atbara scrubland Halfa seemed a haven. Despite these objections, the Government decided that they would settle at Khasm el-Girba.

The material and human issues at stake in the decision are difficult to equate but there is good reason to believe that the Halfawis will in the long run have a better life than they had in Nubia. Certainly those moving from poverty-stricken villages cannot be worse off. To that extent the Government's plan was wise, but it had unfortunately to deal with the people of Wadi Halfa, the most prosperous of the Nubians and the most comfortably settled, who could see no possible advantage in moving and thought at first they might expect another Halfa to be built somewhere on the Nile. The decision was bitterly opposed by them on the general grounds that they were being asked to adopt a new way of life in a hostile and unfamiliar climate. Late in 1960, four Ministers went to Halfa to reason with the people but, at the same time, to correct the impression that there was any question of choice about the site of resettlement. When it became clear to the people that Khasm el-Girba was irrevocably chosen, riots broke out in the town and the ministers were temporarily detained as hostages against a new decision by the Government. The disturbances were quickly quelled and the ministers went free, but the troubles spread to Atbara, Khartoum and Omdurman. Nubians and university students who sympathized with them were in daily clashes with the police for a fortnight, in the course of which about forty were arrested and twenty were taken to hospital. One of the people arrested was Mohammed Tewfik, himself a Halfawi, who was Commissioner of Labour. During this period, Wadi Halfa was put under military rule and its communications with the rest of the Sudan were cut. Towards the end of the fortnight, the railway workers of Atbara widened the protest demanding an end to the military Government and the abandonment of the High Dam scheme. For a time the situation was serious enough for the Government to consider postponing the visit of President Nasser, which was due to take place in the following month.

The next three years were spent convincing the Nubians that the move to Atbara would be worth while. Their objections were manifold, ranging from protests against the alleged unhealthy climate of Khasm el-Girba and the inadequate compensation being offered them particularly for their treasured date palms, to superstitious anger at the coming submersion of the tombs of their local saints. The last point caused serious unrest which only subsided, it was reported, when an archaeological expedition discovered that a fourteenth-century monk had been the object of worship in the tomb of the venerated Sheikh Feweiss el-Karny.[1] Doctors insisted that Girba was one of the healthiest regions in the Sudan, completely free of mosquitoes, flies and other disease-carrying insects, and parties of Nubians were taken down to see for themselves. The Government paid compensation for the 37,000 palm trees in the Halfa region and conceded that the Nubians should not pay the difference between the value of the new house in Girba and the house left behind, so that they moved unencumbered by debt. The compensation awards totalled in the end £S8 million, or just over £S150 a head, in addition to the land and houses provided in Girba.

The conversion was nevertheless extremely slow and towards the end of 1962 there were still only about 5,000 who were willing to move. How many availed themselves of the one choice open to them, of taking cash compensation and moving away from the Halfa region on their own, has never been stated, but 5,000 Egyptians at Halfa remembered in 1964 that they were Egyptians and entitled to emigrate under the Egyptian scheme to Kon Ombo on the Nile. In Halfa-Degheim only 383 of the 525 house owners opted for Khasm el-Girba, the remainder asking for compensation in cash, and the people of Hasa village made what the Government called 'unreasonable demands' at the very last minute and had to be warned of the difficulties they

[1] Fomil Labib, in *Al-Mussawar*, Cairo, February 7, 1964.

would face if they did not move in time. In the end it was the inevitability of the change that wrung reluctant consent from most Nubians who, when faced with the alternative, the disintegration of their close-knit communities, decided to move together to the Atbara.

The resettlement was planned by the Government to preserve the communities, by providing New Halfa as the central town and 26 villages named after the villages left behind in Nubia, each to hold 250 families. The economic possibilities were very much better because the flat scrubland beside the Atbara offered very much wider opportunities for irrigation than did the narrow strips of land alongside the Nile. The main resettlement site covered 180,000 acres and when immigration began in 1964 there were 90,000 acres of land prepared for the main crops, cotton, wheat and beans, which are being grown under Government control by rotation. (The Government has also started its own scheme for sugar cultivation and built a sugar refinery.) Each family was given an acre of land for the private cultivation of fruit and vegetables.

The first view of the resettlement area was drab and inhospitable to the Halfawis, used as they were to the rich green palm groves, the rocky banks and islets of the Nile and the rolling sandhills enclosing their private world and their straggling villages, which might have grown out of the ground. The flat and open landscape left them without protection and the uniform rectangular villages, with straight streets, the water tower and the central square, lacked the liveable untidiness they were used to. There was an old Khasm el-Girba village with its indigenous inhabitants, but the settlement area was uninhabited, and, like a vast new housing estate where nothing has had time to grow, was drearily inhuman in appearance.

The initial unattractiveness was inescapable and time and communal life, the Nubians' natural talent for decoration and the colours of crops in the fields, will soon soften the harsh barrenness. The Government offers in the meanwhile a better material life and has gone to great expense to ensure it. The compensation paid by Egypt for the flooding of Nubia was $42 million but the cost to the Sudan will be in the region of $140 million before the scheme is completed. There will in the end be thirty-two schools, thirty-three hospitals, dispensaries and health centres and a mosque for every village, and with the equivalent of fifteen acres for every family, the Nubians should achieve new standards of living. In the long run the resettlement may bring the migrant menfolk back to their families, for the scheme was devised to accommodate all the Halfawis, of whom 38,478 actually lived in the Wadi Halfa area and 14,796 retained their Halfa homes but worked elsewhere.

A new dam at Khasm el-Girba is the economic foundation of the resettlement project. It will store nearly 1,500 million cubic yards of water, enough to irrigate and reclaim half a million acres, and generate 7,000 kilowatts of electricity. Three hundred engineers and technicians from Italian contracting firms, working with 1,300 Sudanese, were compelled to work night and day to finish it in time. Even so, there was almost disaster in 1963 when an unusually powerful flood on the Atbara broke the upstream coffer dam and washed the debris into the dam's flood gates.

The entire resettlement scheme seemed in jeopardy, for not only was work on the dam delayed by the damage, but the building programme at the site was in such difficulties that for a time it seemed unlikely that it would be possible to rehouse the people from Wadi Halfa before the High Dam lake engulfed their homes on the Nile. The £13 million sterling contract for all the villages at Khasm el-Girba had been given in 1962 to a British firm, Turriff Construction (Sudan) Limited, who set about preparing the foundations at the site while they prefabricated the buildings in England. Difficulties began for Turriff, shortly after the contract was signed, with the Sudan Government's dismissal of the German consulting engineers. When during the following summer the Government complained that Turriff were not building fast enough, the company contended that they were being asked for a faster rate of construction than was provided for in the contract. The Government nevertheless proceeded to transfer 4,200 of the houses to nineteen Sudanese contractors leaving only 2,300 for completion by Turriff.[1] The

[1] Turriff claimed £3 million from the Sudan Government for breach of contract and at the time of writing it seems probable that the financial dispute arising from the affair will go to arbitration.

dislocation of the scheme was so serious that the Sudan asked the U.A.R. at the end of the year if the flooding of the Wadi Halfa region could be delayed, a request which could only have been granted by delaying work on the crucial first stage of the High Dam. As the Russians and Egyptians at the dam had only then got firmly in sight of their target date for diversion of the Nile after two years of unremitting labour, the Egyptian Government naturally refused.

Turriff were well prepared to hurry forward with their part of the programme but the Sudanese firms, few of which had experience of work on such a scale and at such a speed and all of which had come to the task very late in the day, were driven to make superhuman efforts to fulfil their schedule in the few months left to them before the migration started. Building standards inevitably suffered and when the first heavy rains struck the Atbara forty of the houses were so badly damaged in the first village to be settled that the occupants were made homeless.

The first intention to begin the orderly evacuation of Wadi Halfa early in 1963 was made impossible by the time taken in planning, but there could be no mistake about the 1964 date, for the lower part of Wadi Halfa itself and the villages north of it would be submerged by the lake formed against the High Dam coffer that year. In these circumstances, the apparently impossible had to become possible, and in January 1964 the first party of 1,175 people left Wadi Halfa by train for their new homes on the Atbara. The resettlement area was far from complete, but there were houses and living was possible.

Thus began 'the biggest planned human migration', as the Sudan Government described it. The inhabitants of the two villages of Faras and Serra, who farmed fertile strips of land near the Egyptian border, were moved with all their possessions and livestock on trucks to Wadi Halfa, where they boarded the train for Khasm el-Girba. Only the very old and very sick, who were taken by plane, were exempted from the long, overland journey. A doctor and midwife travelled on the train with the party and guides were provided to instruct the people about conditions in their new area and what they must do on arrival. Three more trainloads were moved before the beginning of the Moslem fast of Ramadan, when the migration was suspended until the fast finished twenty-nine days later. Then it was resumed and three times a week the trains transported the Nubians across Dongola into Khartoum and then over another 250 miles of desert to the Atbara.

Wadi Halfa began to die; by the end of May even the boats to and from Shellal ceased to run and fewer and fewer people moved about the silent streets as all departed except the handful who had planned their future for themselves. Whole villages were left empty to the waters of the Nile which, slowly and relentlessly, began to climb the banks.

The evacuation of Egyptian Nubia was a more orderly affair because the U.A.R. planners, who assumed from the outset that the High Dam would be built on schedule and wasted no time thinking further about it, began their work in 1961. They selected as the site for resettlement a crescent of land about forty miles long bordering the Nile in the region of Kom Ombo, which is about thirty-five miles north of Aswan. There was no nonsense over consulting the Nubians about it; only when the operation had been prepared in great detail were the representatives of the villagers called to discuss the design of the houses to be built and to see whether anything more could be done to meet their wishes within the general framework of the plan. The houses were designed on the pattern used in Nubia, each with a compound surrounded by high walls, one side of which gave access by separate doors to the rooms. One of them was built as a pattern for the Nubians to examine and only slight alterations were required to make it suit their needs.

There were undoubtedly many Egyptian Nubians who were willing to move to better conditions lower down the Nile, for the change in their case was nothing like as drastic as that offered the Sudanese and they would be nearer than before to their migrant relatives in Cairo. The old folk naturally disliked it, but three times before their people had moved away from the rising waters of the Nile and they accepted this fate with resignation. They may even have been conscious that the final evacuation was only hastening a natural process, for as many Nubians lived temporarily or permanently away from home as remained in the villages. When a plebiscite among the 48,000 inhabitants was held, 15,000 out of 16,000 families agreed to be resettled and all but 172 families chose to have compensation in kind instead of cash. On the count of consent the U.A.R. Government had little to worry about.

The resettlement area was named New Nubia and each of the thirty-three villages was given the name of the old village from which its occupants would come, with the addition of the adjective 'new'. The villages were also established in the same order as they had in Nubia, so that New Debod was at the extreme north of the crescent and New Fereg far south, just as the old Fereg was near the Sudan frontier. In this way the relations between village and village as well as the family grouping of villages were preserved, and sometimes even strengthened by the proximity of each new village to its neighbours.

The houses were built of stone, without any wood in the roofs to be destroyed by the soldier ants and other insects, and so were more durable than the mud-brick structures they were replacing. They consisted of units of one to four rooms, each unit within its compound, and were built in Nubian fashion, facing north to get the cool breezes. It was not always possible to keep the houses of relatives in close proximity to each other but an effort was made to do so as far as possible. The Government even uprooted palm trees and replanted them at the new site in order to preserve some economic value from the old area and to give an air of maturity to the new. But they were essentially planners' villages, where the maximum and most careful use of the available space had from the outset been of great importance, and the final result, as in the case of Khasm el-Girba, was a geometric arrangement which, despite all the efforts, bore no visual resemblance to Nubia.

The planners, starting from virgin desert, were able to provide amenities which many villages in Egypt still lack and which the Nubians almost entirely lacked at home. Each village was provided with a primary school and a public health unit, its guest house, market and bakery, and a sports field and mosque. Water was led by pipes to the villages and roads connected them to the main highways. There were, in addition, regional amenities directed from the administrative headquarters of New

Nubia, known as Nasr City, including four multiple rural centres of the type provided elsewhere in Egypt (at which agricultural and craft training, medical supervision and other rural services are provided under one roof), a central hospital, secondary and teacher-training schools and police stations. The cost of constructing New Nubia was just over £E13 million, but this is not the end of the programme. The Government has plans to provide homes and services for the Nubians who were not residing in the villages in 1960, who number again about 48,000, in the hope that the migration and emigration of the Nubians will be reversed by the opportunities offered in the new communities. One provision of the basic law stipulates that the owner of the land must also work it, so that a Nubian who takes a plot will be unable to migrate for long periods to the towns of Egypt or sell his land to other Egyptians.

Preparation of the resettlement site was well advanced, even to the supply of water to some of the land prepared for irrigation, when the time came to begin the evacuation of Nubia in 1963, but it was at this stage that trouble developed between the Government and the evacuees. The number to be moved was not quite as great as in the Sudan, and the distance to be travelled by the people of the most distant southerly villages was only 300 miles, but the rules and regulations governing the evacuation were resented. To some extent the Nubians, when faced with the prospect of leaving their familiar surroundings for ever, caused the difficulties themselves by making demands on the officials that could not possibly be met, certainly at so late a stage, but this did not prevent them from accusing the officials of inhuman behaviour. There were, however, many difficulties caused by bad organization and administration on the Government side.

The committee responsible for the evacuation used six large boats, ten buses and twenty large trucks, but the transport was not always available on the appointed day and for several days afterwards, so that the villagers, with their homes dismantled, life disorganized and the supply cut off to the village of food – often a place well out-of-the-way – found themselves temporarily homeless and with nothing to eat; or they would be moved at the correct time only to find that the amenities of the new village had not been completed and they were without water, food, fodder or a roof. These situations were often made worse by the Nubians, whose migratory relatives returned from the towns and cities of Egypt to help in the removal but who also helped to overcrowd the transports and devour what food was available.

Altogether about 100,000 tons of goods and chattels and the livestock had to be moved with the families and the practice of the committee was to move the people, their possessions and their animals in separate boats to Aswan. The animals were there put into quarantine and the people and the possessions transported to the Kom Ombo area by bus. The Government would have preferred the Nubians to slaughter their livestock against compensation, but most of them valued their animals so highly that they insisted on taking them with them, despite the knowledge that very early began to seep back to them that large quantities were dying in the quarantine and many more at the new villages. The Government had warned of these disasters, pointing out that the Aswan quarantine, which had been built for the normal trading movement of animals, was not equipped to take so many livestock, and that in the resettlement area there was unlikely to be enough animal fodder for two years. As most of the Nubians could not afford to buy fodder from outside the area, it is improbable that many of the animals which survived the move were saved for the future.

The head of each household was given an acre of land to start with and ultimately, when sufficient water is available from the dam and the ditching and canals are complete, the intention is to raise each holding to between three and five acres, in accordance with the provisions of the Agrarian Reform Law. They will not be allowed to farm freely as in Old Nubia, for they will be brought into the co-operative system which operates in the regions of agrarian reform, and when they have received their full allotment of land they will be compelled to put 40 per cent down to sugar cane. Kom Ombo is the sugar centre of Egypt.

Each family was maintained by the Government for three months after arrival in New Nubia, although they had been given the impression that they would be fed until they reaped the first harvest. On the face of it, the decision not to do so seemed harsh, but in fact the Nubians were no worse off than they had been in their old villages where 70 per cent of the income came from remittances from their relatives in the towns.

Measured against the problems involved, the evacuation of nearly 100,000 people with their possessions and animals has been a remarkable feat, achieved with surprisingly little trouble and certainly without any irreparable disaster. It may well prove a remarkable social development, in which the strange and isolated lives of the Nubian peoples are transformed. Persistent migration of menfolk to the towns, forced on them by economic necessity in the first place, should cease as the greater economic opportunities of Khasm el-Girba and Kom Ombo are achieved. The unnatural lives of the women, separated from their husbands and living solely as the wards of old relatives and the mothers of children, should no longer be necessary.

These incidental benefits of the High Dam are not, however, likely to be achieved quickly. There are no signs yet that the Nubians living in the towns are anxious to come to Kom Ombo, for migration has become a way of life as well as an essential way of earning money; but it may well be that, away from the isolation of villages high up the Nile and in closer contact with the relative sophistication of Kom Ombo, the effect will be to increase the tendency noticeable in recent years for Nubians to emigrate altogether, taking their wives and families with them to settle in the towns.

The basis of the resettlement programme in both Egypt and the Sudan is agriculture, but the Nubians who have scrabbled a meagre living on little land, are not great farmers although they have always farmed. They are honest, clean, and can be industrious, but in their old villages they were the greatest congregation of remittance-men to be found anywhere.

Their world is, in any case, now disappearing for ever. In a few years' time the lake behind the High Dam will stretch from hill to hill across the Nile valley in Nubia and the landscape will consist only of sand and rock, offering to the onlooker perhaps a gaunt grandeur but nothing else. In the years to come, those who travel by boat from the Dam into the Sudan will travel through an empty world, with the mud-built villages dissolved beneath them, palm trees rotting deep in the water, and a few solid buildings like the hotel at Wadi Halfa lying well below their keels as ghostly havens for Nile fish.

While Nubia dies, the town of Aswan sheltering behind the two great dams and gazing south along the emptiness of the lake, flourishes and finds a new way of life. As the first and direct beneficiary of power, it is growing rapidly into an industrial town.

Aswan is the gateway into Nubia. For centuries the main town was situated on Elephantine Island, in the middle of the Nile, which in antiquity was known as Yebu, or elephant land, perhaps because part of it resembles an elephant in shape or because it was the trading-post for the tusks and hides of elephants brought from the lands of the blacks. It was always a frontier town, at first standing guard at the edge of the known world, then in later antiquity commanding the last and most northerly cataract as the final defence against marauders or the terminus for the trade in gold, ivory, ostrich feathers, tamarins and skins. As pharaonic Egypt declined and Nubia subsided into its long, long, sterile sleep, Aswan ceased to have much military significance, but as the effective limit of Egypt it remained a trading-post and the town grew on the east bank which is present-day Aswan. The trade in gold was gone, but at the end of last century *Baedeker* was still able to inform tourists of its commerce in ivory, ostrich feathers, tamarins and skins from the Sudan and Abyssinia.

When the Mahdist revolt engulfed the Sudan, Aswan became again the frontier defence, where British and Egyptian troops stood guard. On the bare ridges behind the Cataract Hotel there are the remnants of the fortifications raised when Kitchener was commander. In those days the bazaars of Aswan were full of dervish trophies, swords and spears from the battles of Kosti and Abu Klea, bloodstained jibbehs, coats of mail and hide shields broken by British bullets. The *Baedeker* of 1898, telling tourists once again of the journey southwards through Nubia, noted that 'inconvenience from the Mahdists is no longer to be feared, since British troops are stationed at Wadi Halfa and Dongola'. But the Mahdist revolt and Port Sudan built by the British on the

Red Sea, had at last deprived Aswan of its trade in ivory, ostrich feathers, tamarins and skins. It lived by the rich and the sick who passed their winters in its dry, warm climate. It slept through the heat of the summer.

Although Aswan had been big enough in early Arab times for 20,000 of its inhabitants to die in a single plague attack, it had only 6,500 at the turn of the century. In the peace of this century, living on agriculture and tourism, the people multiplied until they numbered 30,000 at the time of the 1952 revolution, but it was still a quiet oasis in a monotonous yellow countryside, with its main street strung along the river-side, the post office, the hotel and the governate all just as and where they were at the time of Kitchener, and with some of the shops still bearing the same names.

Now the population, excluding those who are working on the High Dam, is over 40,000, and the town is still growing as Aswan becomes the nexus of an industrial region based on the hydro-electric power of the two dams and the iron ore found there. Already over 500,000 tons of ore are mined each year, and in Aswan town itself a big new suburb has been built adjoining the Kima fertilizer works. The fertilizer plant will be expanded when the power from the High Dam becomes available and the machinery for other factories, including one for the manufacture of packing paper from the waste of the sugar cane, has already been ordered. Tourists will still go to Aswan for its climate and its antiquities, and no doubt to see the High Dam itself, and in due time they will be able to sail down the lake into the Sudan over the palm trees and debris of the villages of Nubia and the town of Wadi Halfa; but their starting-point will have greatly changed. Aswan has wakened from its long sleep.

CHAPTER TWELVE

The Stuff of History

The Nubian earth was of little value to the people who scratched a living from it but it is a multi-palimpsest in stone and paint of unique value to the historian. It is littered with the shards and tools of unknown primitives and its tombs and temples are illuminated with inscriptions and paintings of ancient civilized men. Paint which has survived the ravages of time tells how people lived and fought. A builder records his work, a trader his travels, a warrior his conquests, a viceroy his rule and an emperor his supremacy over all mankind, and the idle, scratching his trivialities just as any vandal tourist might carve his name on a choir stall today, accidentally casts his tiny light on a facet of history. There are 1,200 Greek inscriptions in Nubia, most of them no more than a few casual words, but combined they make a notable contribution to the knowledge of Ptolemaic times. Often a layer of paint or plaster removed from an ancient wall will reveal another even more ancient, and almost everywhere one site is laid on another, so that the valuable known impedes the way to the equally or more valuable unknown. This is the stuff of history and it is condemned to drown in the lake rising behind the High Dam.

During the European Ice Age, the Atlantic rainstorms broke over North Africa and where there is now desert there were rolling grassland, parks and rivers. With the withdrawal of the ice cap from Europe about 15,000 years ago, North Africa slowly dried out and its inhabitants scattered in search of life-giving water, some across island stepping-stones to Europe and some into the Nile Valley. The cycle of human progress was resumed in new environments. In Europe there was steady erosion of savagery from the southern seaboard; on the Nile it was, in terms of history, awesomely fast and culminated in the pharaonic civilization which endured for three thousand years. It was overtaken at last by Greeks and Romans from across the sea and a great merging of human intelligence and skills took place on and from the Nile.

Nubia, that stretch of the river between Aswan and the third cataract which is precisely the part to be covered by the High Dam reservoir, was for long ages a frontier of the world. The earliest prehistoric human industries were found in East Africa, but related industries have been identified in Egypt and near Khartoum and it is a reasonable assumption that Nubia was not just an empty space between prehistoric peoples. Probably the same type of people lived beside the river all the way from the third cataract to the sea until at some time the natural barriers on the border march exerted themselves and the connection was broken somewhere near Aswan. The people to the south were left far behind in the advance of Egyptian civilization but new peoples brought other primitive African cultures to them. The timid imprints of prehistory suggest that early peoples met on the Nubian Nile and mingled their blood, their words and their cultures, and, therefore, that the vital missing link in human knowledge, the significant step from the primitive to civilized man, might well be hidden there. It is, indeed, a reasonable conjecture that the role of the region then was consistent with its role in the period of known history, when it undoubtedly was the melting-pot of peoples and cultures.

Tribal remains in the desert have thrown some light on the progress made before the pharaonic civilization and by the time the pharaonic story acquired recognizable shape progress was already considerable. The river-banks were probably pocked with petty principalities, each worshipping its own gods but all sharing a common culture. From time to time no doubt some of them were fused together by the overlordship of powerful men, until about six thousand years ago Menes united for the first time 'the two kingdoms' of upper and lower Egypt with its southern frontier near Aswan. For centuries all contact had been lost with Nubia, or Kush as it was called, but the wealth of civilized Egypt created a market for the products of Kush and a trade link was forged. The caravan route became the route of conquest, as the Egyptian kings, attracted by the gold, the ivory and other exotic products, decided to take the land for themselves.

The tide of history rose and fell on the Nile in Kush. Only

once, during the strong eighteenth dynasty, were the pharaohs able to penetrate beyond the third cataract to conquer Kush, but equally the kings of Napata once conquered and ruled Egypt for a hundred years. The true frontier of Egypt was in the vicinity of Aswan and when the pharaohs ruled in Kush it was by means of strong fortresses built forward as far as the second cataract. The border march was divided round about Faras, which is on the frontier of the modern Sudan and was in those days the fulcrum of conquest and retreat. Forces from the north swept on beyond Faras whenever they were strong and their base stable enough and they fell back on Aswan whenever their strength failed.[1] The Kushites themselves, as the strength of the Egyptian defences prove, were a powerful people. Their monarchy was eventually overthrown by forces from Abyssinia, but by that time Egypt had been conquered by the Greeks and the Romans, and the emperor Diocletian had withdrawn his forces for ever from the region south of Aswan.

As with wars, so with people. There is as yet little knowledge of the cultures that bridged the gap in Nubia between prehistory and the dynastic age of Egypt, but there is known to have been a 'copper age' people, whom archaeologists have called the 'A' group because they know nothing of their origins. These people were contemporary with the earliest dynasties in Egypt and were themselves already on the road to civilization. Trade goods from the Old Kingdom of Egypt have been found in their graves alongside fine burnished pottery, carved stone and copper tools. Another unknown people (called the 'C' group because earlier historians wrongly thought they had discovered a 'B' group) occupied lower Nubia to its limit at Faras in late Old Kingdom times and their traces did not entirely disappear until the reconquest of Kush by the eighteenth-dynasty pharaohs. In the Roman period a race of nomads known as the Blemmyes took their place in the history of Nilotic Kush by harassing the garrisons and it was because of them that Diocletian withdrew behind Aswan. With the decline of the Meroite kingdom, an-

[1] History repeated itself near the end of last century when Anglo-Egyptian forces fell back on Aswan during the Mahdi rebellion; they advanced to Wadi Halfa but had modern engineering, in the form of a railway, to carry them forward beyond and away from the difficult border march on the river.

other intruding people, called the 'X' group by archaeologists, over-ran Nubia and left evidence of their existence in numerous tumuli. These may have been the people identified by the Romans as Nobatae, who seem to have been constantly at war with the nomad Blemmyes and worshipped Isis at the Temple of Philae until they were driven from the island by the Romans in the time of Justinian.

Nubia languished, apparently forgotten by the ambition of kings and princes but was still a very real frontier, this time for the faiths of mankind. The new religion of Christ was established in Abyssinia and Egypt and travelled along the Nile, but it took 400 years to impose itself from the north on the people beyond the first cataract. Islam took even longer. Moslem armies that stormed across North Africa and into France and Spain, failed to subjugate the people of Nubia entirely and the whole region did not fall to the Moslem faith until the conquests of Ismail Pasha, son of Mohammed Aly, about 150 years ago. A Christian kingdom flourished on the Blue Nile well into the Middle Ages. The Nobatae, who were converted to Christianity in the sixth century, constructed churches and monasteries and converted pagan temples to their new religion in Nubia, many of which were fortified against the Moslems who had conquered Egypt.

Such greatness as Nubia intermittently possessed has long since vanished and sand and time have combined to obliterate much of the record, leaving only the remains of mud-brick buildings to carry a pettier tale of the border march onwards into the modern world. Its importance to the story of man remained. Prehistoric tribes moved about the region, leaving dim traces of their simple skills and way of life. Only the strongest conquerors failed to falter in the wilderness between the first and third cataracts. Cultures met and merged and parted again, leaving the dregs of their meaning in fragments of stone, inscriptions, pictures and monuments. Faiths lingered long in isolation from the spiritual changes outside. The tide of affairs rose and fell there for so long a time that it deposited the material constituents of the history of mankind from the primitive to the civilized.

Archaeologists, anthropologists, social historians, all recognized the importance of Nubia. 'Egypt is the cradle of Mediterranean civilization and the archaeologist's living book of history', said Christiane Désroches-Noblecourt.[1] 'Its scattered pages discovered one by one were pieced together and read with patience and devotion and now constitute the most prodigious and profound chapter on remote antiquity. But despite the wealth of material found, many pages are still missing. . . . Not all the treasures of Nubia have yet been discovered. Those that do remain are of such vital significance that it is our duty, regardless of nationality, to help in preserving them. For they are links in a great chain which is significant and meaningful only by their cohesion'.

There are few people who have seen the wonders of Nubia when they stand revealed for a few months each year, for those months are the hottest of all, when only the hardiest traveller ventures south from Aswan. It is the period of the flood in Egypt north of the Aswan barrage. When the weirs are wide open and the red waters flowing freely, the level of the river south of the barrage falls and hundreds of monuments, tombs, fortresses and temples 'often surpassing Gothic cathedrals in size'[2] re-emerge from the almost empty basin of the Aswan reservoir. That they have survived the inundation at all is almost entirely due to Gaston Maspero, Director General of the Egyptian Antiquities Services, who hurriedly had them consolidated before the second heightening of the dam, but his work would have been impossible had the temples not been constructed of the finest and most resistant sandstone.

The monuments will never again re-emerge from the even greater reservoir of the High Dam, because its primary purpose is to preserve the water from year to year on a 'century-storage' system. Further, the higher level of the lake will engulf monuments more to the south and at higher sites, many of which were hewn out of the friable sandstone cliffs and could not survive the submersion. All structures of sun-baked clay submerged in the earlier flooding were lost and more of them are dissolving now as the High Dam lake rises; they cannot be preserved except in documentary form.

Because the tide of history ebbed and flowed in Nubia, the

[1] Curator of Egyptian Antiquities, Louvre, in *The U.N.E.S.C.O. Courier*, February 1960.
[2] Ibid.

sites have no chronological order on the Nile and many of them have historical periods laid one on the other. The very first monument, the beautiful Philae on an island at Aswan, links the Egyptian pharaonic times straight through to Rome, and in the middle of Egyptian Nubia stands the fortress of Kasr Ibrim which was occupied intermittently from pharaonic times to the Arab conquest and occupation. A great many of the monuments were converted to Christian purposes by the Copts as they extended Christianity.

It is almost impossible to list the relics of the past, for the hundreds of minor sites are as important to the historian as some of the greater and the innumerable prehistoric remains are nameless. Yet some idea of the wealth of material can be gained from reference to the main monuments. Going southwards from Philae, there is the lovely little kiosk of Kertassi whose walls are covered with Greek inscriptions; the Greco-Roman temple of Debod; the almost complete temple of Kalabsha, which the Emperor Augustus rebuilt, and near-by the temple of Beit el-Wali with its religious pictures as clean and clear as they were when painted thousands of years ago; Dendur, one of the monuments taken over by the Copts but which was earlier dedicated to two Roman heroes who were deified by Augustus; the six temples of Ramses II on the top of a cliff near Gerf Husein; Dakka, dedicated to Thoth, the God of Writing; Wadi es-Sebua, with its avenue of sphinxes, partly hewn out of rock for Ramses II and later covered with important Christian paintings; the fortress of Ikhmindi built to defend the local people from the Blemmyes; Korosko and the 3,000-year-old temple of Amada; Derr, cut out of the rock, again for Ramses II; Aniba, the capital of Lower Nubia, once the home town of the Viceroys of Kush whose tombs and palaces have not yet been found; Kasr Ibrim; and, finally, the stupendous twin temples of Abu Simbel – finally only because it is the supreme ornament of Lower Nubia and not far from the Sudan frontier. It is appropriate to start with Philae and end with Abu Simbel but there are, as there are everywhere, more monuments and relics on the rest of the route to the frontier.[1]

[1] I have written of the sites here as they were before the start of the *U.N.E.S.C.O.* campaign.

Although a century or more of research had revealed a great many of the secrets of Egyptian Nubia, it was well known to the scholars that there were sites which had not been touched or which could yield a great deal more; and there was the problem of preserving those monuments that should and could be saved. The situation was much more lamentable in the Sudan where, up to 1960, only ten sites had been partially excavated in the 115 miles of Sudan that would be flooded by the High Dam lake, although a cursory survey had revealed 100 sites and there were almost certainly more. They included seven ancient towns, four pharaonic temples, twenty Christian churches, rock graves of the eighteenth Egyptian dynasty, early Christian rock chapels and sites with rock drawings and rock inscriptions. Sudanese Nubia also contained the complex of fortresses in the region of the second cataract with the immense base fortress at Buhen, opposite Wadi Halfa. Buhen alone was being completely excavated and studied because Professor Walter B. Emery began there in good time, but the other fortresses at Semna, Kumma, Mirgissa, Dabanarti, Shelfak and Uronarti had been only partly investigated. Associated with some of them, notably Buhen, were small temples which Professor Emery calls the garrison churches.

The Sudan had been given belated attention by scholars as compared with the long period of work in Egypt but its importance was quickly realized when the region was doomed by the dam. Here, if anywhere, could be found evidence and knowledge of the merging of African cultures with the civilization of Egypt and, through Egypt, with Europe, and preceding any civilization but almost certainly leading to it, there were the Palaeolithic and Neolithic peoples who had left their significant traces in Sudanese Nubia. One site was proved to be over 8,000 years old.

Slowly, patiently, carefully, the fragments of the past in Nubia were being garnered and studied to compose the story, for there seemed ample time for the work ahead; it was always possible to excavate tombs and temples from the sand, to record and sometimes preserve them. Then, suddenly, the High Dam promised to submerge everything. All would be lost. Even if submarine exploration proved possible on the Nile there would be little or nothing to find. Mortar and plaster would crumble and tumble, walls would be washed clean of paint, rocks and their inscriptions would be eroded, the contents of graves would be scattered.

This, then, was the fate that faced Nubia, a frontier of the ancient world and a frontier of the modern mind no less. So great was the challenge that scholars of all nations united to mount the most remarkable study of history that has ever been known.

The preservation of monuments, though it costs much, satisfies artistic sensibilities and enlivens the mind of the serious tourist, is not the vital purpose of this campaign. It is, as the record implies, to save as much as possible of the sum of knowledge. The scholar is, indeed, less sensitive than the layman and, if necessary to his purpose, will himself shovel back the sand over monuments he has laboriously unearthed once he is satisfied that he has drained it of truth. The world looks at pylons and paint while he looks in wonder at the ancient, shabby skeleton of a horse that has no right in the ruins. The trophies of the campaign will not be in the form of valuable antiques, but in words, diagrams and pictures which a decade hence may still not be complete.

There is nothing of intrinsic value to be unearthed in the study of prehistory and little to be said about it that will stir popular interest, but the prehistoric surveys in Nubia which, because they approach the least known past, must be counted among the most important efforts now being made. Too little is known of it and far too little time now remains for all the study required. There are terraces doomed to inundation which have surface indications that people lived there in the Old and Middle Stone Ages. Pebble tools which might be contemporary with the first East African finds have been located near the second cataract and near by there are tools known to belong to various later periods which suggest that an important prehistoric transitional phase might be traceable. The earliest pottery and fishing tools found near Khartoum and elsewhere should also be found on the Nubian Nile. Stone implements, pottery, bones, oyster shells, ostrich egg shells, all in association with rock carvings, have been found at three sites. Prehistoric artists scratched hundreds of thousands of geometric and abstract designs, and pictures of boats, animals and birds, in the region between Wadi Halfa and Aswan alone. All of this indicates that there were numerous New Stone Age communities living in Nubia and encourages the view that there was continuous occupation of the region from earliest times.

Knowledge inevitably declines as one probes back in time and in Nubia it also declines in travelling south. The more powerful flow of history from the north has left the greatest traces, so that the density of historical deposits thins out along the line of the river until it disappears at the third cataract or is overlaid by the traces of the northern movement of people and culture from Black Africa. Although it is a single border march, the story of which needs to be read as a whole, Nubia can be divided between Egypt and the Sudan, with the richest monuments lying on the Egyptian side.

Egyptian Nubia has been studied as intensely as any comparable region of the world, partly because the wealth of its ruins were known and attracted the first archaeologists, partly because they have been continuously accessible since the days of Napoleon, but not least because the building of the first dam at Aswan and its subsequent heightenings compelled the scholars to make urgent efforts to examine and record the remains that would be lost in the reservoir. Nevertheless, there are pages missing from this much-thumbed story, such as the whereabouts of the influential Viceroys of Kush between the eighteenth and twentieth dynasties, who are believed to have lived at Aniba, between Aswan and Wadi Halfa. Only one tomb has been found, that of Pennut, although these chiefs of Egypt's African territories must have had palaces and tombs befitting their status and dignity.

The knowledge even of known sites south of the Egyptian frontier was scanty, because few had been completely excavated. Some knowledge of them was naturally acquired by excavations in Egypt, to which it was so closely linked through history. For two thousand years or more of the first pharaonic period the record depends largely on trade goods used in the barter between Kush and the Old Kingdom and found in tombs. It was not until the twelfth dynasty that the region began to be lavishly documented in stone and on stone by the pharaohs who founded the Middle Kingdom and forced their way into Kush, but their fortresses on the frontier, which provide a rich source of historical material, have only recently, and not entirely, been unearthed from beneath the ruined fortifications of the triumphant eighteenth dynasty. The link of knowledge between the two periods of conquest is tenuous in the extreme.

The eighteenth, nineteenth and twentieth dynasties made their contribution in tombs and temples of historical value and great beauty – it is to this period that the magnificent rock temples of Abu Simbel belong – but these were essentially an extension of known Egypt into Nubia. When the Nubians themselves were later in the ascendancy they built temples in the Egyptian style and carried their mixed pharaonic and African culture south to the sixth cataract, but so far very few remains of the Napatan kings have been found in the region of Wadi Halfa where they might be most expected. The Meroitic kingdom left graves, but the key to their cursive script, which has been located as far north as the second cataract, has never been found.

The tide of history ebbed and flowed so strongly between the second and third cataracts that the relationships of peoples and societies should be most strongly marked there. One is compelled to say 'should be' because there has not yet been sufficient exploration to put the matter beyond all doubt. It is, for example, possible that the earliest history of Africa could be illuminated from this reach of the Nile, because here the facets of revealed African cultures could be dated by relationship with the known history of the region.

The High Dam suddenly confronted the scholar with the extent of his ignorance, the gaps in his knowledge, of an area which was well known in comparison with other regions of research. At least he knew where he was going until the High Dam barred his way. The traces of prehistory, the links with black Africa ranging forward to the kingdom of Meroe, the unidentified intruding peoples, the way of the Christian and the Moslem; the life of the Kushites themselves, their wars with Egypt and the conjunction of the two cultures: these were some of the problems in the broad stream of history from the primitive to the civilized that he was seeking to elucidate with a patience made possible by unlimited time and usually forced on him by limited funds. Overnight he found there was no time for patience. He must harvest his knowledge as best he could before the flood came.

The antiquity of Egyptian Nubia was better known than any similar region with the exception of other parts of Egypt but the very richness of its relics imposed an immense problem of rapid documentation. It contained also some monuments of such outstanding beauty, grandeur and historic interest that it was inconceivable to imagine that they could be utterly destroyed. It seemed to many that to permit their destruction would condemn this generation as vandals of the worst kind.

Before Nasser could make history with the High Dam he had to find the money. The scholar was in no better position. In order to conduct the research and to save the monuments in the time available he required more funds than had ever been given for scholarship before and which could only be obtained by the combined efforts of the nations of the world. Thus Nubia, poor, forgotten and now doomed, commanded in its dying days the interest of mankind.

CHAPTER THIRTEEN

The Scholars' Campaign

Long before the High Dam became a serious proposition and therefore a threat to Nubia, Mme Christiane Désroches-Noblecourt, curator of Egyptian antiquities at the Louvre, was deeply concerned about the decline of archaeological research in Egypt caused by the obstacles that the Egyptian Government had put in the way of international expeditions. She advocated the formation of a Documentation and Study Centre where the art and civilization of ancient Egypt could be recorded in complete and accurate detail and made available to the scholars of the world, and when Mr Saroit Okacha became Minister of Culture in Egypt her initiative and persistence were sustained by his enthusiastic support. In 1955 he persuaded the Egyptian Government to finance and form the centre and, with support and technical assistance from U.N.E.S.C.O., the Department of Antiquities quickly got to work. In this unspectacular fashion the great campaign of the scholars to save the treasured past began.

Once the fate of Nubia was sealed in 1954 by the decisive events of the autumn, it was in the interests of both Egypt and the Sudan to secure international co-operation, for their combined resources were insufficient to save the ancient wonderland of Kush. The Sudanese Minister of Education complained that he knew little about the situation until the following year, but there was no doubt among the experts in Cairo about the effect of building the dam. The self-interest of Egypt was therefore engaged at last in the proposals which Mme Désroches-Noblecourt advocated, so that the centre, designed as a permanent instrument of recording and research and now housed in a modern building near the Egyptian museum, was directed at once towards the pressing needs of the campaign. Even the Suez affair, in which France and Egypt were at war and which caused the expulsion of French people and the seizure or sequestration of their property, did not end the co-operation of the French in this respect.

In one other case the Suez affair accidentally contributed to the salvaging of Nubia before the world campaign got under way. Professor Walter Bryan Emery, of the Egypt Exploration Society of London[1], reputed by many to be the greatest Egyptological explorer of the day, was, as an Englishman, excluded from his life-study of the Sakkara necropolis and turned to Buhen, across the Nile from Wadi Halfa, which he had for long had in mind. Buhen, which had been partially excavated twice before, was the base fortress and town of the pharaonic era at the second cataract, which had been built in the twelfth dynasty, destroyed by the Kushites, and recaptured, rebuilt and enlarged by the eighteenth dynasty. It consisted of one layer of ancient military history laid on another and the town outside the wall of the stronghold covered about a square mile of desert. There was neither time nor need to excavate the whole town, but by reason of the early start on the work, Professor Emery was able to complete one of the most notable excavations of all time, which laid bare the temple and the remains of the two forts and enabled him to reconstruct on paper the defensive system of both pharaonic periods. It is highly improbable that so thorough an operation could have been effected by the most expert exploration that started as late as 1960. These two enterprises, the documentation centre and Buhen, were major achievements preceding the campaign and they were merged with it. At the same time the Departments of Antiquities of both Egypt and the Sudan, which were also continuously working to the limits of their modest resources, were absorbed in the major effort.

It had been intended that the centre should first record the monuments at Thebes, but when it came into being in Cairo in 1955 the threat to Nubia inherent in the High Dam altered the priorities and it was immediately given the task of collecting full documentation of the sites in danger. Its experts embarked on a Nubian survey, copying inscriptions and making photographs and colour slides, but valuable as this work was, it could not save the monuments or investigate the unexplored or partly explored sites. Therefore in 1959, when Russian money made the

[1] Edwards Professor of Egyptology at London University.

High Dam possible, Saroit Okacha appealed to U.N.E.S.C.O. on behalf of his Government for international assistance and within three months the Executive Board authorized the Director General, Dr Vittorino Veronese, to prepare for the campaign. In the meanwhile, U.N.E.S.C.O. secured the agreement of the Egyptian Government for the French *Institut Géographique National* to undertake a photogrammetric survey of the area for the preparation of maps.

The Sudan Government later asked U.N.E.S.C.O. to extend its campaign to cover its part of Nubia which, if less rich in remains, contained numerous archaeological and prehistoric sites which had so far been little studied. The Sudan Survey Department carried out an aerial survey in 1956–7 and secured the services of a U.N.E.S.C.O. expert to prepare an archaeological map, but it had insufficient funds or staff to prepare a photogrammetric map, which was essential to research. U.N.E.S.C.O. reported that unless the utmost use was made of the little time remaining there would be no hope of further important discoveries in the Sudan 'like the recent one of the fortified site of Buhen'. Ziada Arbab, the then Minister of Education, pointed out that the lack of intensive research in the Sudan of sites from prehistory to modern history offered enough prospects to encourage the interest of learned circles.

Dr Vittorino Veronese convened a meeting of thirteen international experts in various fields of study, who met in Cairo in October 1959, to decide what excavations should be made, which monuments could be preserved and which removed to new places of safety, what other measures were necessary, and how much the work would cost. At this meeting Saroit Okacha declared formally on behalf of the Egyptian Government that excavators could keep half of their finds except those which were unique or essential to complete the Egyptian collection, that it would authorize future researches outside the threatened area, such as Sakkara,[1] and would cede certain temples for transfer abroad to museums or scientific institutions open to the public. This undertaking removed the obstruction to international

[1] As a result, Professor Emery returned to explore Sakkara when his part in the Nubian campaign was finished.

archaeological research in Egypt. The Sudan Government gave a similar undertaking.

U.N.E.S.C.O. had a dual role. In the first place it had to encourage governments and organizations throughout the world to provide the money, without which there could be no campaign, and in the second to provide material and technical assistance and act as intermediary between the subscribers and the Egyptian and Sudanese Governments to ensure that the funds were correctly spent. Its committee of experts advised the director regarding the work, and in the pursuit of the money Veronese formed an International Committee of Patrons with King Gustav VI of Sweden as chairman, and an International Action Committee which established liaison with national committees. The U.A.R. and Sudanese Governments, which still had the last word on what should or could be done, formed international consultative committees of experts, the membership of which overlapped to a large extent with those of U.N.E.S.C.O.

This hurried organization was to be modified as the work proceeded but for the time being it was enough. On March 8, 1960, the scholars' campaign to save the monuments of Nubia was duly launched.

> 'The dam' [said Director Veronese in his appeal], 'will bring fertility to huge stretches of desert; but the opening of new fields to the tractors, the provision of new sources of power to future factories, threatens to exact a terrible price. ... It is not easy to choose between a heritage of the past and the present well-being of a people, living in need in the shadow of history's most splendid legacies; it is not easy to choose between temples and crops. I would be sorry for any man called on to make that choice who could do so without a feeling of despair; I would be sorry for a man who, whatever decision he might reach, could bear the responsibility for that decision without a feeling of remorse.
>
> 'It is not surprising, therefore, that the Governments of the United Arab Republic and Sudan have called on an international body, on U.N.E.S.C.O., to try to save the threatened monuments. These monuments, whose loss might be tragically near, do not belong solely to the countries who

> hold them in trust. The whole world has a right to see them endure. They are part of a common heritage. . . . Treasures of universal value are entitled to universal protection. . . .
>
> 'Moreover, it is not merely a question of preserving something which might otherwise be lost; it is a question of bringing to light an as yet undiscovered wealth for the benefit of all. . . . A new era of magnificent enrichment is thus opened in the field of Egyptology. Instead of a world deprived of a part of its wonders, mankind may hope for the revelation of hitherto untold marvels. So noble a cause deserves a no less generous response'.

These were most modest words to launch a campaign which in both money and archaeological scholarship transcended anything the world had ever seen or might ever see again. Without taking account of excavation, research and recording, the campaign required $87 million for removing and preserving monuments, which was more than Britain and the United States had offered for the first stage of the dam itself and as much as Russia offered to begin the building of it. It required, in addition, the biggest assembly of scholars to work for years on the enterprise, under conditions of great heat and often hardship, with every hour counting against them. 'An effort of co-operation has never been undertaken on such a scale in the domain of archaeology', reported the Director General to U.N.E.S.C.O.; and the U.A.R. international committee of experts declared themselves 'conscious of the magnitude of the Nubian task. For full success, more time and more wisdom are needed than we can command . . . The task is truly formidable and the time is frighteningly short'. This was the judgement of some of the world's greatest specialists.

U.N.E.S.C.O. launched a world-wide campaign to interest all peoples in the work ahead. It sponsored National Action Committees to further the campaign and within a year they were operating in twenty-two countries. It published numerous booklets and pamphlets and secured the support of the Cultural Committee of the Council of Europe, and private bodies in various countries began to raise money. Journalists and television cameramen were induced to visit Nubia to see and photograph the monuments for themselves. Brazil made an immediate contribution of $35,840 which financed the preliminary stages, Belgium, Yugoslavia, Holland and West Germany promised funds and Congress asked President Eisenhower to submit before March 1, 1961, a programme of financial aid. U.N.E.S.C.O. dipped into its own pocket to provide the essential preliminary credits so that the work would not be delayed. The Aga Khan was appointed 'special adviser' to the Secretary General and in this role visited the Sudan and Sweden and spent September propagating the Nubian need in the United States. U.N.E.S.C.O. mobilized its senior officers to visit as many countries as possible and Egypt sent its exhibition, 'Five Thousand Years of Egyptian Art' on a world tour starting at Brussels, and later the Tutankhamen jewels and other precious objects, starting this time at Washington. The operation became so big and widespread that René Maheu, the Deputy Director General of U.N.E.S.C.O. established a special department under J. K. van der Hagen to direct and supervise the Nubian project. It was a publicity campaign of unparalleled dimensions that no single private enterprise in public relations could ever match either in scale or cost.

It was possible to determine the priorities with accuracy, because the lake behind the High Dam, beginning to rise in 1964, would submerge monuments at increasingly higher levels on the banks and farther to the south as far as the Dal cataract until its maximum height was reached after 1970, but historic judgement and artistic taste and the need for exploration at some sites, also influenced the order of salvation. The first task of the U.A.R. Committee of Experts was to determine what must be done and in what order.

Professor Emery was appointed chairman of the sub-committee for plans and priorities and member of the related sub-committee for personnel and materials. One of the first decisions of the parent body was to form a *sondage* expedition to make a survey of Egyptian Nubia. Professor Emery, who prepared a statement of its methods and principles, deserted Buhen temporarily to launch the survey in January 1961. It was led by Professor H. S. Smith, who had with him four other experts and thirty labourers. Starting at the Sudanese frontier, the team worked northwards on both banks of the river, and completed its work in November of the same year. It was a skilled and speedy operation for which the Egypt Exploration Society received the commendation of the Committee of Experts. The report of the expedition was published early in 1962.

The Cairo headquarters of the documentation centre were built by the Egyptian Government specifically for the purpose of archaeological studies and records. It has now a five-cabin boat, the *Horus*, for its teams in the field, and a floating laboratory, constructed by the Egyptian Government to precise specifications, containing workshops, offices, library, storage space and living quarters, which is towed as a self-contained unit to moor against the sites where work is in progress. The records are finally assembled at the centre and, to safeguard them against loss, are copied on microfilm. In 1960 the operations had not reached this advanced stage, but because of the foresight of Mme Désroches-Noblecourt, the centre was almost ready to bear the burden imposed on it. From its Cairo headquarters it maintained a flotilla of boats on the Nile, its staff of Egyptian and foreign archaeologists, its reconnaissance patrols and its working parties, keeping them supplied with everything from food to the technical equipment needed for their work. In this form it constituted an entirely new weapon of scholarship. It made a complete and accurate study of the great temples of Abu Simbel, every minute detail of which was examined, recorded and photographed. Archaeologists, philologists, architects, photographers, draughtsmen and moulders, armed with cameras, generators and searchlights, turned the temples into film studios while they assembled black-and-white and colour photographs, photogrammetric negatives, architects' notes, casts and copies of hieroglyphic texts and rock inscriptions that ranged through pharaonic times into the Christian era. 'Photogrammetry', by which it was possible to produce minutely exact models from two stereoscopic photographs, was carried out by the French National Geographic Institute with startlingly successful results.

As soon as the campaign got under way, the centre's order of work was altered to suit the priorities, being switched at once to temples that would be first threatened by the floods, such as Debod, Kalabsha and Wadi es-Sebua. Its knowledge of the field of work gave it an importance transcending that of simple recording and Mr Louis A. Christophe, the U.N.E.S.C.O. representative resident at the centre, was made the permanent secretary of the Committee of Experts. Quiet, unobtrusive and efficient, this small and modest man still plays a vital role that will outlive the campaign itself. He laid down the principles governing the documentation of temples, inscriptions, graffiti and rock drawings, explored the possibilities for epigraphic survey when none was offered from outside, and co-ordinated the epigraphic work himself. In the middle of 1961 he issued the edict to all in the field that all scratchings and rock engravings, from prehistoric through protohistoric to pharaonic times must be copied. A year later he was able to report that three-quarters of the work was completed and the centre was busy preparing an archaeological map of Egyptian Nubia. By this time there were experts from Italy, Poland, Austria, Spain and France co-operating with the Egyptians at the centre.

The Sudan was much less ready for the challenge, although its Director of Antiquities, Thabit Hassan Thabit, had wasted no time in calling for aid. Its international Committee of Experts was not formed until October of 1960 and in place of the carefully designed documentation centre in Cairo, it had an improvised clearing-house of records and information known as the Field Office in an old building in Wadi Halfa. Nevertheless, two U.N.E.S.C.O. experts, W. Y. Adams, an American, and H. A. Nordstrom, a Norwegian, laboured unceasingly with Dr Thabit in the office and in the field, and were described in due course by the Committee of Experts as 'undoubtedly among the best specialists in Nubian archaeology and in that capacity more or less irreplaceable'. The Antiquities Service, the Sudan Survey Department and Adams and Nordstrom prepared an immense aerial map of the sites which was laid out in the only large room of the office, where maps and very full documentation of Nubian antiquities, published and unpublished, were assembled.

Sadiq Hassan Abdallah, Sudanese irrigation specialists, warned the experts that the whole area north from the Dal cataract would be affected by the flooding and that, as most of the monuments were of mud-brick they were hardly likely to survive the first flood. The Sudan Government stopped all field work elsewhere in the country and increased the allotment of funds to the Antiquities Department sevenfold, but this was still too little in men or money for the work ahead.

The Egypt Exploration Society was working at Buhen but otherwise there was not a single outside offer of help for the Sudan. The needs were manifold. In the first place the stone and painted temples of Buhen[1], Semna East (Kumma), Semna West and Aksha had to be saved, probably by dismantling them and removing them to a new open-air museum being built at Khartoum, and the fine wall paintings at the church of Sheikh Abdel Gadir and in the eighteenth-dynasty tomb at Debeira East needed to be salvaged. It was doubly important that the temples should be moved quickly because there were earlier sites beneath them that required to be explored. U.N.E.S.C.O. had anticipated the problem by sending Dr Pietro Gazzola, a specialist in architectural restoration, who had surveyed the temples and reported that it would cost about $770,000 to remove and re-erect them.[2] The fortresses of mud-brick could not be saved and therefore required thorough architectural surveys so that at least on paper they would not be lost; in this respect the work at Buhen was the model and it was suggested that a section of the Buhen fortress walls showing the advanced military construction should be carefully cut out and transported to Khartoum. There was an immense amount of exploration to be done as the survey of Dr Adams and his team showed, including excavation of the first bishopric of Nubia in a big mound at Faras, which was likely to be the first site submerged in the Sudan. As for the scores of smaller sites for which there was never likely to be any foreign aid, Dr Adams and his survey team dug them as carefully and as quickly as they could in passing by.

The scholars began to move into Sudanese Nubia late in 1960. Warsaw University sent a team from its Centre of Mediterranean Archaeology to Faras, the Argentine University of La Plata combined with the French National Excavations Commission

[1] The Buhen Temple was eventually transported and re-erected at Khartoum by the Egypt Exploration Society with funds provided by the British Treasury.

[2] Director of Fine Arts of Verona and Inspector General of Department of Antiquities.

to excavate at Aksha and Mergissa, the Spanish National Committee sent a team to excavate Irgin, a combined mission from the Scandinavian countries set to work on a series of sites, moving south from Faras East, the Oriental Institute of Chicago University began to excavate at Serra East and the Ghana Government sent a mission to Debeira West. All this was not enough for the task, but even so it was the most remarkable assault on the archaeological sites of the Sudan that had ever taken place.

Prehistoric exploration was recognized from the outset as a separate operation in both Egypt and the Sudan, although the Experts Committee asked the expeditions to investigate any remains they came across in the course of other researches. Professor Emery did not engage a prehistorian for his *sondage* expedition because he contended from the outset that a prehistoric survey required a large group of specialists working independently. As no offers to survey the remains of the sequence of Stone Ages had been received by January 1961, the Committee asked Professor Gerhard Bersu of Frankfurt (Main), a West German member of the U.N.E.S.C.O. International Committee of Monuments and Excavations, to take charge of this problem and instructed the U.A.R. Department of Antiquities to co-ordinate prehistoric work. Professor Bersu reported in the summer that the survey should be entrusted to Professors Solecki and Fairbridge of Columbia University and the U.S. National Science Foundation promptly offered $40,000 towards the cost. Solecki undertook to spend several seasons on the work of Stone Age surveys in both Egyptian and Sudanese Nubia and Robertson-MacKay of London, Inspector of Ancient Monuments and Historic Buildings, offered to work with him. Solecki's preliminary work was completed in the region of Abu Simbel early in 1962, by which time Yale University and Toronto University of Canada began to mount jointly an expedition to survey the Middle and Late Stone Age remains. They co-ordinated their operations with those of the Columbia University team which had begun prehistoric research between the frontier and Wadi Halfa in Sudanese Nubia. The Toronto and Yale experts also asked permission to explore the Kom Ombo area, which would be lost to exploration by the resettlement of the Nubians, because this region was important to the study of Early and Middle Stone Age cultures.

The expedition from the Museum of New Mexico came strongly into the field in 1962 and by the 1964 season had twenty specialists working in five separate groups to excavate the pre-historic sites located in the earlier years. Professor Shiner, the leader of the Museum's expedition was astonished by the richness of the 'finds' and by the end of 1964 his teams had cleared no less than 200 sites. All the evidence pointed to the fact that the Nubian plateau was at one time a congenial living place, with several great rivers cutting across it, for habitation sites were found 10 miles out from the Nile in the dessert, where no one could survive today.

The prehistoric expeditions had some of the toughest work in the whole campaign and when they moved from the river into the desert were sometimes in danger from bedouin who ranged there; Toronto and Yale 'may benefit from association with the Desert Institute and need guards', the U.A.R. Experts Committee calmly noted.

The effort was so complete in Egyptian Nubia that the Experts Committee was able to decide in 1962 that no more concessions would be granted except for Jebel Adda, the one remaining site of high promise which no mission had yet undertaken to explore. The position in the Sudan was still much less happy. 'Many requirements have not been met and further assistance is still essential to accomplish the remaining tasks', reported the Minister of Education, Ziada Arbab. The work of exploration was not even keeping pace with the discovery of new sites. The indefatigable Dr Adams located no less than 250 sites and did work on all of them except those which the foreign expeditions asked to be added to their concessions. Haste often compelled incomplete operations. In its rapid progress southward from Faras, the Scandinavian expedition located 170 sites, which proved only to be 80, and it was unable to make architectural records of churches and monasteries or comprehensive copies of rock drawings in the time available. The Sudan Survey Department produced maps and photographs which provided an excellent topographical basis for the expeditions and continued to photograph the sites under excavation, but Dr Adams and his team could not maintain an adequate records office at Wadi Halfa when they had so much field work to do. In 1962, therefore, the Sudan Experts Committee was still asking for a fully staffed documentation centre, backed if possible by the French, to be established in the new museum at Khartoum.

Furthermore, no firm offer had been made to save the temples, whereas in Egypt, the salvage operation, leaving aside the great temples of Abu Simbel, was three-parts committed and in many cases well under way. Dr Harold J. Plenderleith, Director of the Rome International Study Centre for the Preservation and Restoration of Cultural Property, who had been enlisted as special consultant on the Nubian monuments, confirmed in his report that the fortresses in Sudan could not be saved and that the sandstone of the Aksha temple had so deteriorated that it could not be moved without turning to powder[1], but there were other temples, including Buhen and church frescoes and tombs that could be saved although in the case of Buhen he advised its transfer to the hill-top instead of to Khartoum.

The highest priority in Egypt was accorded to the beautiful temple of Kalabsha which, lying forty miles south of the dam, would be the first submerged, and the West German Government undertook to pay for, remove and re-erect it. (By the autumn of 1963 it was standing proudly on a hill on the west bank of the Nile overlooking the work at the dam – already a point of call for those tourists who got a permit to visit it.) The Egyptian Department of Antiquities did a great deal of this work itself, removing stone by stone the temples of Debod, Taffeh and the kiosk of Kertassi in barges to Elephantine Island in September of 1961. In the following year it transferred the pylon of the Dakka temple and the small temple of Maharraqah and asked the Swedish firm of VBB to carry out technical studies for the transfer of the tomb of Pennut from Aniba and the monuments of Beit el-Wali, Wadi es-Sebua and Abu Oda. The U.S.S.R. and Netherlands joint group undertook to dismantle and move the Dakka temple but this proved impossible.

The salvage of the temple of Amada, on the west bank of the Nile about 120 miles south of Aswan, was one of the remarkable

[1] Aksha temple was successfully removed to Khartoum at the expense of the French Government.

engineering feats associated with the Nubian campaign. This temple was built over 3,000 years ago and contained seven exquisitely inscribed and painted halls. The U.A.R. Antiquities Department dismantled the front of the sanctuary and then in 1964 French engineers transported the rest of the temple as a single unit for a distance of 1½ miles, raising it at the same time a distance of 215 feet, out of reach of the rising river. The removal was made inch by inch along rails, the immense bogie being driven by hydraulic pumps which activated hydraulic jacks anchored to the rails after each tiny movement. The cost of this removal was $237,000.

The most notable group of monuments, on the island of Philae, could not be in any danger until very late, when the reservoir behind the dam would be full in about 1969, but its salvation was already assured on April 7, 1961, when President Kennedy proposed to Congress, with every certainty of acceptance, that Egyptian pounds to the equivalent of $10 million should be set aside for saving Nubian monuments, 'particularly Philae'.[1]

The extent of international action in Nubia has overshadowed the work of the Departments of Antiquities in both Egypt and the Sudan, but both of these were engaged to full stretch from the outset of the campaign and their experts were continuously in the field, either on exploration, work of co-ordination, or in maintaining supplies to the expeditions already at work. Both Governments were fully committed. The Committee of Experts recorded their thanks to the U.A.R. for an efficient service of boats, 'a most urgent need', which had been provided in all phases of the Nubian campaign. Three passenger steamers capable of carrying seventy-two people each were fitted out for the journey from Aswan to Abu Simbel and back in one day. It took the Egyptian bureaucracy a long time, however, to get into

[1] One offer from the United States was refused. The enterprising Parker Pen Company proposed to dismantle and transfer the temple of Dendur to Janesville, Wisconsin, at its own expense. This, however, was small beer compared with the offer of an unnamed American for Philae itself at the turn of the century. 'I am assured that an American has offered to buy the temple for £40,000 and carry it off to Chicago, an offer which naturally has no chance of being accepted.' (A. B. de Guerville, *New Egypt*, 1905). M. Maspero believed that he could move the Philae temple in those days for £40,000.

phase with the Government's effort. The international teams had constant trouble with visas, were expected to pay taxes on the incomes, which were in most cases provided by foreign contributors, and at first were not allowed customs remission on the equipment and materials they needed for their work.[1] The Sudan Government was more helpful in all these matters: visas were granted for long periods at a time, there was a 50 per cent concession on all travel costs inside the country, and all scientific equipment was admitted free of duty. The comparison did not redound to the credit of Egypt, and it made it appear that the Government – which in fact contributed more money than any single country to the campaign – was trying to profit in cash from the help given it.

When the autumn season of 1962 opened there were expeditions from twenty-two countries, the entire antiquities services of Egypt and the Sudan, and many scholars who had privately volunteered, all at work along the Nile in the most remarkable harvesting of history the world has ever witnessed. It began in committee rooms, with distinguished archaeologists, zoologists, architects, epigraphists and cartographers, who were used only to their own tidy and limited expeditions, becoming overnight tycoons in historical research. The opening studies often read like the launching of industrial enterprises, in their lists of cranes, generators, pumps, tractors, refrigerators and photographic equipment, and of the mechanics and drivers and technicians to go with them; they talked in hotel lobbies about sums of money they had never before thought of. It was a race against time, with each act governed by priorities imposed by the flood to come, and passions were deeply engaged in every aspect of the enterprise. Yet the scholar-tycoons invested both the drama and dimensions of it with studious calm, as though they were opposed by nature to the indecent haste of their own attack on the tranquil monuments. Out in the field, time and the ageless river seemed to impose a proper silence for there the workers could only make haste slowly; nothing could be rushed. At some sites the seemingly leisurely line of labourers would carry their small straw baskets of sand and dirt from a hole for the experts to sift

[1] Most of the experts, including those of the Egypt Exploration Society, gave their services free, receiving only their modest expenses.

for the smallest grain of history, as though years counted for nothing; at another a graphologist would sit hour by hour patiently copying an inscription with minute exactness; architects carefully directed the dismantling of stone temples that had stood untouched except by time for thousands of years, marking each piece to reassemble them later; hundreds of camera shutters clicked the day through; planes droned overhead at 3,000 feet to get vertical and oblique shots for the perfection of maps. With the sharp fall of dark each day, the scholars would adjourn to their tents, their boats or their improvized houses, and with generators drumming electric light to them or paraffin gas lamps hissing overhead, would scribble diligently at notes and sketches. In Wadi Halfa and in Cairo, and in universities and learned institutes all over the world, the mountain of paper rose to proportions that already promised decades of study after the scene of the labours was lost for ever.

CHAPTER FOURTEEN

The Price of History

While the scholars worked with tranquil diligence in Nubia, the accountants of U.N.E.S.C.O. were counting the cost with frenetic diligence in Paris. Although many of the expeditions were financed directly by government or private sources, such as the American prehistoric researches and the Buhen excavations, it was evident from the outset that much greater sums than these would be needed if the campaign was to achieve its targets. In particular, the protection or removal of the monuments selected for preservation was estimated in 1961 to cost $87 million, of which nearly $70 million was required for saving Abu Simbel alone. The U.A.R. Government undertook to provide $20 million (which it later increased by another $1·5 million) but the amount to be raised elsewhere was still considerable.

It was hoped that the world-wide publicity campaign launched by U.N.E.S.C.O. – it alone was estimated to cost over a million dollars – would raise the money in voluntary contributions, but the initial surge of interest subsided in the mid-summer of 1961. M. Rene Maheu, the Acting Director General, reported in June of that year that the results were 'encouraging' but he could not disguise the fact that the funds were a long way short of the target. It was, in fact, evident that voluntary donations were unlikely to save Nubian history from extinction and M. Maheu went on to say that 'the financing of the preservation through international co-operation could not be guaranteed unless the Governments of member states of U.N.E.S.C.O. agreed to share the financial responsibility between themselves in proportion to the contributions to the organization'. It was the opening shot in a new campaign to secure levied contributions which in time was to reveal how many countries had reservations about the whole affair.

This first crisis over cash nevertheless revived the appeal. The Consultative Assembly of the Council of Europe invited its

Committee of Ministers 'to recommend that members' Governments give most urgent thought to all possible means of giving further practical support' and nineteen member States of U.N.E.S.C.O. offered help in one form or another as against sixteen who said they could do nothing. Pope John XXIII gave $10,000 and a surprising contribution of $40,000 came from the little state of Qatar on the Trucial coast of Arabia, which was not a member of U.N.E.S.C.O. and seemed culturally as remote as possible from the scholars' campaign. In September the United States Congress decided to allocate $4 million, apart from $6 million for Philae and any future contributions to Abu Simbel, of which $2·5 million would be for saving monuments and $1·5 million for U.S. missions in the field. Twelve months later, twenty-three countries, other than the U.A.R. and the Sudan, had undertaken to pay $1,712,000 to the Nubian general account over the years of the campaign. This was the account in which funds not committed to any particular project were held. In addition to the U.S. contribution, West Germany promised $3·5 million, of which $1·6 million was earmarked for the transfer of Kalabsha temple, and Italy $1·6 million. France also undertook to move the Amada temple at a cost of $240,000. In August M. Maheu was able to report that 'it is now certain that almost two-thirds of the temples can be transferred. Thus the financing of the Abu Simbel lifting operation remains the main problem. . . .' The Sudan was still, nevertheless, the poor and forgotten relation, for not a single offer had been received for the transfer of its five temples, the total cost of which Gazzola had estimated at a mere $770,000.

The U.N.E.S.C.O. Trust Fund consisted of three separate accounts: first, for saving Egyptian monuments, second, for saving the Sudanese monuments, and third, to hold contributions for unspecified purposes; but in addition to these accounts there was considerable expenditure on survey, documentation and exploration which took the form of direct financing of the expeditions in the field. In 1962, the commitments of institutions for this work was more than $1 million for twenty-two of the twenty-nine countries taking part; the other seven did not provide their figures. The largest single contribution was that for the work of the Egypt Exploration Society which, spent and to be spent, was £28,000, about $78,400.

Britain came to the help of the Sudan by undertaking to move the Buhen temple at a cost of £8,000, an act of grace which short of actual shame could not be escaped after the work of Emery there[1]. Holland also undertook to spend $120,000 on the transfer of one of the Semna temples, giving the Sudan at last some grounds for hope that its little needs would be met. The fact remained, however, that Maheu's remark that the salvage of Abu Simbel remained 'the main problem' was a notable understatement: both in technical difficulty and in cost it was *the* problem. By July of 1962 it seemed obvious to everybody that the money for this task was not going to be raised by public appeals to people or governments. There were, indeed, a great many highly civilized people who asked whether, in a world where there was still so much want of the simple necessities of life, it was justifiable to spend so great a sum on saving a temple, every microscopic detail of which had already been recorded.

Such doubts could not concern U.N.E.S.C.O., for it had been launched on a campaign which did not permit exceptions. M. Maheu reported that 'it must be recognized that the safeguarding of Abu Simbel temples, despite the special efforts made in that connection, is still encountering great difficulties. . . . To date, U.N.E.S.C.O. has thus called for voluntary contributions. . . . It may be assumed that the secretariat has exhausted possibilities offered by this procedure.' There was, in fact, almost nothing at all available for Abu Simbel and the $37,000 spent by the U.A.R. on expert consultants to consider the problem of lifting the temples and on the equipment and materials for consolidating them prior to lifting, had been advanced by U.N.E.S.C.O. and recovered from the account for unspecified work. M. Maheu, who was not prepared to let the matter rest there, embarked on a personal campaign to raise the money by other means, and first sent his financial experts to banks in various countries to see if U.N.E.S.C.O. could raise a loan.

He stated:

'. . . The most desirable and practical procedure would doubtless be for the general conference (of U.N.E.S.C.O.) to

[1] The removal of Buhen actually cost £8,000, about $22,400.

include, in the regular budget of the organization, for the requisite number of years, appropriations to pay interest and amortization on advances. . . . The only difficulty at present concerns the amount, which does not appear to be overtaxing the possibilities of international co-operation. Of course member States who have made, or will be making, voluntary contributions will be entitled to deduct the amount of these contributions from that fraction of the annual interest and amortization which they will be obliged to pay under the regular budget.'

The U.A.R. Government, which had undertaken to contribute $11·5 million to the Abu Simbel operation, further eased the financial pressure by reporting that the saving of Abu Simbel could be done in two parts, the raising of the temples and then the reconstitution of the site, the second having no urgency because it would be carried out above the limit of the reservoir and could be partly financed by contributions from the Egyptian people themselves. Therefore, the immediate need was to raise $42·6 million, of which $11·5 million was already assured from the U.A.R. Government. The figures had become more manageable but there was no escape from the fact that the member States would be 'obliged' to provide the money under the new scheme. The matter was also urgent. The U.A.R. Government wanted assurances that if it gave out work on Abu Simbel the money would in due course be provided and, as things stood, there was going to be a heavy deficit in 1963 which U.N.E.S.C.O. could only meet if it were allowed to raise credits.

At the end of October 1962, U.N.E.S.C.O. took stock of the financial position. It proposed first that the publicity bill for $1·3 million should be cut to $600,000 and met from the U.N.E.S.C.O. budget, and in the light of experience it estimated the cost of transferring monuments, excluding Abu Simbel and Philae, would be $8·8 million instead of $9·5 million. The new estimates, therefore, were $42·6 million for Abu Simbel, $6 million for Philae, $8·8 million for salvaging other monuments and $600,000 for miscellaneous expenses, mainly publicity. The cost of Philae was underwritten in its entirety by the United States Government. For Abu Simbel there were, in addition to the U.A.R. contribution, a West German offer of

$1,845,000 and from Italy another of $1,760,800, of which $160,000 was from private sources. There was still, therefore, a deficit of $27·5 million on the amount needed for Abu Simbel. Contributions to the fund for other monuments now totalled $5·7 million but there was, in addition $1·6 million which had been contributed without special assignment,[1] leaving a deficit of $1·5 million. The total deficiency was $29 million, but as the U.S. and U.A.R. contributions were in Egyptian currency, no less than $19·5 million constituted the shortfall in foreign currency requirements. It was calculated that U.N. special agencies would be able to use $1 million in Egyptian currency a year for eight years, offsetting this sum with foreign exchange, so that the net need for exchange was $11 million. The U.N.E.S.C.O. secretariat had secured assurances from Italian banks that they would together provide $10 million over five years, leaving only $1 million of foreign exchange to find, if the member States of U.N.E.S.C.O. would underwrite the bank loan.

By this remarkable sleight of hand U.N.E.S.C.O. had managed to make the expensive rabbit vanish under the hat but U.N.E.S.C.O. members unfortunately noticed where it had gone. M. Maheu argued eloquently before the U.N.E.S.C.O. Committee of Experts that the burden would not be very great if spread over the 107 members and M. Saroit Okacha stated that there was no alternative except the destruction of the Abu Simbel temples. It duly appeared that the loss of the temples seemed a real alternative to some members. The experts themselves marshalled a formidable array of objections, contending that the loan system would set a bad example, that it was a derogation from the spontaneity of the voluntary system, that the loan repayment, being a first charge on U.N.E.S.C.O., would have a deleterious effect on the U.N.E.S.C.O. programme, that it was unsound because it would entail a long-term debt the *ultimate* size of which could not be foreseen and that it would in

[1] The $5·7 million consisted of the following contributions: from the U.S., $2·3 million for Egyptian monuments and $118,825 for the Sudanese; from West Germany, $1·5 million for Kalabsha; France, $240,000 for Amada; Holland, $120,000 for Semna; Britain, $22,400 for Buhen; Yugoslavia $24,000 for Abd el-Kadir; and the U.A.R. itself, $1·2 million. The contributions for unspecified assignments included $160,000 in Cuban sugar.

any case raise the budgetary requirements by about $2 million a year.

The experts finally suggested that perhaps a cheaper way to save the Abu Simbel temples could be found. Italian interest in the operation – the generous contributions and the loans offered by the Italian banks – must certainly have been motivated to no small extent by the fact that the approved plan for the temples had been put forward by Italy and involved jacking up the temples in two solid blocks from the river-side to the top of the hill, a spectacular feat that would redound to the country's credit for ever more. But it was estimated to cost $63 million of which no less than $38 million would be in foreign currencies. It was the immense price of this project that had the U.N.E.S.C.O. campaign in difficulties.

Certainly the General Committee of the U.N.E.S.C.O. Conference would not decide on the loan scheme, which it referred to the Administrative Commission at the end of November. M. Maheu did his best to convince the Commission that he had not abandoned the system of voluntary contributions but simply needed the loan to make sure that he could make payments in time. The Commission, which clearly had little faith in any reduction of the debt by voluntary contributions in the future, raised the same sort of objections to the plan as had the experts, and when the matter went forward to the Programme Commission in December, M. Maheu, by this time Director General of U.N.E.S.C.O., declared bluntly that the only question was 'to decide whether the desire to save the Abu Simbel temples exists or not'.

U.N.E.S.C.O.'s opinion was reflected in an advance of $800,000 towards the preliminary survey of the temples from the organization's working capital, but well over half the member States, including Britain, had not even bothered to reply to the earlier appeal. Mr Raadi, the Iranian representative on the Programme Commission, expressed very cogently the objections of many states, professing himself 'profoundly' convinced that Abu Simbel should be saved and then arguing that it should not. If it were necessary to save the Nubian monuments, he contended, it was equally necessary to save lots of other things, including millions of ignorant and wretched people who could never know anything about Abu Simbel. U.N.E.S.C.O. had no right to purchase monuments in preference to education for children, and he suggested that the Director General should be equally eloquent in proposing that an extra million or so be raised for education. He proposed that the Commission adjourn *sine die* the proposal for the loan. M. Kuyper of Belgium said the flooding of the temples could have been foreseen from the outset and the U.A.R. should have raised a loan on the security of the new lands to be cultivated from the dam reservoir in order to lighten the claim on international generosity.

In accordance with the Director General's proposal that obligatory loan repayment contributions would be proportionate to the national contributions to the regular budget of U.N.E.S.C.O. and that voluntary subscriptions would be offset against the repayments, there were a few countries, such as West Germany, Italy, Brazil and Czechoslovakia which would not have any repayments to make, and they were inclined to overlook the precedent being set by a compulsory levy. The substantial contributions of the United States were not enough to keep it in the clear because it contributed over 31 per cent of the U.N.E.S.C.O. regular budget and would be called on to pay off 31 per cent of the loan. Britain, which had volunteered next to nothing, would be compelled to repay over $2 million and the U.S.S.R., which had refused to contribute, would have been called on to pay nearly $4 million. Russia bluntly said it would not give anything because it was already helping with the High Dam, a claim that was hardly sound in view of the fact that it had *given* nothing to the dam. It was highly improbable that Russia and the Eastern European countries would have paid their contributions if the loan had been approved, so that the neat project of repayment as set out on paper was unlikely to work. The Programme Commission, in the event, rejected the loan proposal, despite the fact that the Ruler of Kuwait had undertaken to reduce the interest chargeable on the loan by guaranteeing $5·6 million of it. Sr. Pompei, the Italian representative, commented, 'Without a doubt the commission seems to have condemned the temples of Abu Simbel, but it would seem necessary to try and seek once again to what extent the recourse to voluntary contributions is still possible to save them.'

This was precisely what the General Conference did in the following week when it approved a resolution, sponsored by twenty-one states,[1] which did not formally condemn the loan proposal but 'called on member States and their people to take urgent measures for assuring their appropriate participation through voluntary financial contributions and through offers of technical personnel' in the campaign to save the temples. It decided to continue international action 'in so far as may be possible by voluntary means' and requested member States and associate members to inform the Director General what voluntary contributions they were prepared to make and what other forms of assistance they would offer to save Abu Simbel. The Director General was instructed to co-ordinate the replies by March 31, 1963, in order to compose the plan of co-operation so that the U.A.R. would then know the scope and nature of the assurances on which it could rely.

The appeal failed. Britain, the United States and Russia did not reply and Australia and Canada said they could not contribute. France offered to contribute a million dollars in five instalments and contributions from other small countries brought the total contributions, excluding that of the U.A.R., to $7·5 million. At this stage the United States intervened to state that the Italian plan to jack up the temples was impracticable because of the high cost and foreign exchange requirements. The note added that the U.A.R. should consider other solutions and that if an alternative could be found 'the President of the United States is prepared to ask the U.S. Congress to make a contribution in Egyptian pounds towards the preservation of this unique cultural and historic monument'.

A last and urgent appeal was sent by telegram to all the Governments but it was already too late to execute the Italian scheme. The engineers had given several 'final' dates for the signing of contracts but were at the limit when they stated in March that after May 15 it would be too late to save the temples because the waters of the reservoir would rise faster than the jacks could raise the temples. This in itself was not a calamity,

[1] Germany, Belgium, Brazil, Canada, Ecuador, Spain, U.S.A., France, Greece, Guinea, India, Iran, Italy, Morocco, Mexico, Netherlands, U.K., Somalia, Sweden, Venezuela and Yugoslavia.

for it would have been wise to abandon the project a year earlier when the failure of the appeal for funds was known. Quite apart from its excessive cost, which seemed to many nations too much to pay for the salvation of two temples when there were so many other and urgent demands on U.N.E.S.C.O. funds, there was a feeling among many of the delegates that an attempt had been made to stampede them into accepting the plan. This feeling strengthened the reluctance of the United States, Britain and France, and led many African countries which had gone to the conference with the intention of supporting the scheme to absent themselves from the voting.

Other plans had latterly been advanced, and when the failure to finance the Italian scheme became certain, the U.A.R. rapidly transferred its approval to a project proposed by its own technical consultants, Vattenbyggnadsbyran (VBB), to cut up the temples of Abu Simbel, transport them to the top of the hill, reconstruct the temples there, and remake the landscape in the manner of the original site. The total cost of this plan was estimated at $32 million of which $17 million would be needed in foreign currencies. Both these figures were less than half of the estimates for the Italian scheme but it was considered necessary to set aside an additional $4 million as a reserve against unforeseen costs.

It was immediately apparent that the world had a firm idea of what was a fair price to pay for saving Abu Simbel in relation to the many other calls on cultural benevolence. The United States fulfilled its promise to help with a promise of $12 million, there was the standing French offer of $1 million and Britain offered $210,000. The British offer was still less than generous, for Italy promised four times as much and India, Holland and Sweden more than twice as much. Even Yugoslavia and Spain promised more than Britain. Altogether forty-five countries offered just over $19 million and as this was only $1·5 million less than the sum that the U.A.R. had asked U.N.E.S.C.O. to raise and was well within the range of further voluntary subscriptions, the Abu Simbel operation was considered by all concerned as home and dry. The U.A.R. Government pledged itself to meet any shortfall on the fund in addition to the $11·5 million it had undertaken to contribute. The Kuwait

Government finally eased the strain on foreign currency needs by giving the U.A.R. an interest-free loan of £3 million sterling (about $8,400,000), repayable over ten years, beginning 1966.

On November 16, 1963, less than seven months after the total failure of the campaign to save Abu Simbel temples by the Italian scheme, the U.A.R. signed the contracts with Hochtief of Germany, Impreglio of Italy, Grands Travaux de Marseille of France, Sentab and Skanska of Sweden and Atlas of the U.A.R. for the salvage of the temples. At the same time it signed another contract with U.N.E.S.C.O. governing the way in which it would receive the contributions made to U.N.E.S.C.O. There were odds and ends of funds still required for the campaign in Nubia but they were not important; the signing of the contracts was the successful culmination of U.N.E.S.C.O.'s longest and hardest financial haul and they meant that every important part of the work of salvation and exploration in Nubia would be done and done in time. 'Faith has moved mountains', commented M. Maheu.

It was another triumph for President Nasser and his Government but one well enough deserved. From the outset they realized that their own part in the Nubian campaign must of necessity be commensurate with it in size and cost, for it stood most to gain, and it put more men and money into the field than anyone else.

The British Government was, however, miserably parsimonious and only the brilliant work of Professor Emery and his team did something to salvage British honour. There are two countries, Britain and France, which have done more than any other to illuminate scholarship on the Nile by the distinguished work of their Egyptologists, but when this supreme challenge came to crown the work of decades, it appeared that the Government was prepared to let the monuments drown and be damned. Was it, as Philip Cole implied in *The Sunday Times*,[1] that the wounds of Suez still rankled, that Egyptian debts to British people and the feeling that popular opinion was against any kindness to Egypt, palsied the will of the Cabinet? If so, Britain was less generous both in spirit and in cash than France, whose case with

[1] *The Sunday Times*, June 30, 1963.

Egypt was worse, and mundane and temporary considerations were allowed to weigh too heavily against the Nubian mission which, as a wealth of British scholarship had shown, had a meaning far transcending the interests of Egypt. 'It is not a question of helping the Egyptians', said Professor Emery. 'Abu Simbel is part of the history of man – it is a world heritage'.[1] Britain in this affair was something less than civilized.

Sir Mortimer Wheeler, Professor Emery and Sir Frank Francis, Director of the British Museum, met members of the Labour Party Arts and Amenities group and suggested that the British should contribute £2 million (about $5·5 million) over nine years to be spent on British equipment for lifting the temples. Labour Party members determined to press the Government to make a contribution on this scale, considering that, quite apart from the merits of the scheme itself, it would be a great advertisement of engineering skill if Britain could devise the equipment to lift the temples. The party did not fight very hard, perhaps for reasons not very remote from those of the Government, but it was a Labour member, Dr Horace King, who urged that a donation should be given from public funds. When Sir David Eccles, Minister of Education, replied to Dr King in the Commons on July 13, 1962, his words were a self-conscious echo of the arguments of the opponents to the scheme in U.N.E.S.C.O. He said he was not thinking of contributing money from public funds to preserve the temples of Abu Simbel, for, while not disagreeing with the importance and value of these ancient relics, the Government had many claims upon funds to help the masses of children in Africa who needed education.

By the summer of 1963 the United States had promised to pay a third of the cost of a new scheme for cutting and lifting the temples, and Britain was the only major Western country that had so far refused financial help. The international Consultative Committee of Experts for the U.A.R. of which Professor Emery

[1] Quoted by Philip Cole. There were certainly people who opposed any gifts to Egypt. Mr W. Allard, who had worked for seventeen years on the Nile earlier this century, wrote to *The Times* from the Athenaeum Club on June 26, 1961: 'If, however, Egypt thinks it necessary to attract the tourist by giving him something *kolossal*, and *wunderbar* at Abu Simbel, something which the savant and the aesthete will neither enjoy nor need on top of what is available and safe elsewhere, the cost of it should surely be the affair of none except the country in which Abu Simbel is situated'.

was a leading member, had earlier recommended that concessions for excavation outside the threatened region of Nubia should be granted on the basis of the size of the contributions to the campaign. Britain's total aid at that time was £28,000 for the work done by the Egypt Exploration Society, and Sir Mortimer Wheeler was quick to point out that as Britain could hardly, in these circumstances, ask for sites and expect priority, British Egyptology would suffer.[1] Professor Emery, the greatest living expert on the early dynastic period of Sakkara, could have been denied the return of his concession and the Egypt Exploration Society the fruits of his lifetime of study. The diminutive British contribution to Abu Simbel hardly changed the case and when Professor Emery did go back to Sakkara, permission was given out of respect for him and the work the society had done and not as reward for the help of the British Government.

[1] Quoted by Philip Cole, ibid.

CHAPTER FIFTEEN

Abu Simbel

In the year 1812, Giovanni Battista Belzoni was touring the theatres of Britain as The Young Hercules. Dressed in a bizarre costume with a hint of the Orient about it and with a huge plume of feathers adorning his head, he would perform various feats of strength before bringing his act to a climax by cutting a man's head off and putting it on again. At the same time a distinguished explorer, Johan Ludwig Burckhardt, was trekking down the Nile from the Sudan. There seemed nothing less likely than the concurrence of these two lives.

Belzoni, a six-feet-eight-inch giant of a man, was born the son of a barber in Padua, and studied hydraulics in Rome, his father's birthplace. His simple engineering knowledge was in the end to prove of importance to him, but in Rome its only use was to entertain the populace with a few tricks, which earned him so miserable a living that he turned monk. In the light of his subsequent career it was not surprising that he had little liking for the monastic life, and when the French invaders of 1798 secularized some of the Italian monasteries, Belzoni quietly unfrocked himself and went out into the world again. He travelled through Italy and France as a pedlar of sacred relics and images, presumably because they were easier to carry than hydraulic machinery, and, after a fruitless effort to establish a business with his brother in Holland, he arrived in England in 1803.

In that year the Sadler's Wells Theatre reopened with the great clown Grimaldi as Thrumbo in *Jack the Giant Killer* and billed with him as Cormoran the Giant was Giovanni Battista Belzoni. He reappeared later in the show as The Patagonian Samson carrying around the stage eleven men on a heavy iron frame slung across his shoulders. After several months at Sadler's Wells he toured Britain and Ireland, acting with versatility Le Brun's *Passions of the Soul*, performing his strong-man act in an hydraulic extravaganza known as The Great Cascade, which required a magnificent contraption heavy enough to fall through a Dublin stage on one occasion, and playing tunes on glasses, a musical feat reported to be unique in theatrical history at the time. He was next heard of in Spain, where he is believed to have entertained the Duke of Wellington's troops in the Peninsular War.

On his way back to England he encountered Ismail Gibraltar, an agent of Mohammed Aly, viceroy of the Sultan of Turkey and ruler of Egypt, who, on learning that Belzoni had invented a water-lifting device, persuaded him to go to Cairo to design hydraulic machinery for his master. On June 19, 1815, Belzoni arrived in Alexandria, accompanied by his English wife, Sarah, and his faithful young Irish servant, James Curtin. After many delays, which reduced him to desperate poverty, he was at last able to demonstrate his irrigation machine, which lifted four times more water than the *saqia* then in use, but the Luddite temperament of the court circle prevented its acceptance by Mohammed Aly.

Burckhardt, who was already famous in Egypt as Sheikh Ibrahim ibn Abdallah, a Moslem convert, explorer of the Nile and the Sudan deserts, and the first European to make the pilgrimage to Mecca, had already met, liked and befriended Belzoni. He now found him penniless and came once again to his aid. There was at the time great rivalry between the British Consul General, Henry Salt, and the influential French Consul General, a Piedmontese called Drovetti, each of whom was anxious to collect the best examples of Egyptian antiquity for the national museum of his country and the benefit of his own purse. Burckhardt and Salt were planning to bring down the Nile from Thebes the colossal head of Ramses II which was half-buried in the sand there, and the explorer suggested that Belzoni was just the man for the expedition. There was no difficulty in persuading Belzoni, whose taste for adventure was as high as his fortunes were low, to undertake an expedition which required his strength and appealed to his ingenuity, qualities which he was called on to exercise to the full before he got the head to Alexandria on its journey to the British Museum. Belzoni was thus launched on a career which became his passion and, despite the crudeness of his methods, he achieved some notable feats for Egyptology, culminating in the discovery of the entrance to the great pyramid of Giza.

His supreme achievement came between the head and the pyramid. When Burckhardt was travelling down the Nile in 1812 he had paused to examine the smaller temple of Nefertari, which was known to exist at Abu Simbel. To reach it he descended a sea of sand that swept down to the river, and as he was climbing back again he fell in – as he reported in his journal – 'with what is yet visible of four immense colossal statues cut out of the rock at about 200 yards from the temple'. Five years later the British sent Belzoni in charge of a party to examine the site and work began in intolerable summer conditions with the temperature at 112 degrees Fahrenheit in the shade, of which there was none to be had. By this time only the cornice and one of the busts was visible above the scorching sand, but Belzoni succeeded in forcing a tiny aperture giving access to a 'cavern'. Giovanni Finati, chosen because he was the smallest man in the party, wriggled through the hole. His were the first human eyes for hundreds of years to gaze on the fabulous temple of Abu Simbel. The whole party was able to enter the temple on August 1 and found the interior, which had been closed by the sand for so long, as hot as an oven. Henry William Beechey, who had been commissioned to do the drawings of the interior, ruined his notebook with his own perspiration. Belzoni returned to Cairo to give his report on the supreme work of Ramses II, one of the most beautiful and astonishing creations in the world, but the moment of triumph was ruined for him by news that his friend Burckhardt had died without knowing the temple had been entered.

For almost the rest of the century, Abu Simbel was the vanishing wonder, for it was the characteristic of the site that the sand perpetually swept down to blanket the façade. Belzoni did a prodigious job of clearing it, but it is probable that no one saw the temple again until 1844 when the famous Egyptologist Lepsius cleared it once more. In 1869 the Director of Egyptian Antiquities, Mariette, reopened the temple for the visit of the Empress Eugénie. After another twenty-three years the sand was removed again and some restoration done to the façade, but on this occasion a British engineer, Captain Johnstone, built walls on the plateau to protect the temple from the drift of sand. Alessandro Barsanti did some more clearing in 1909, discovering in the process a small court to the north of the terrace, and restored and improved the protecting walls on the plateau. Since 1892, and more particularly since the Barsanti expedition, both temples of Abu Simbel have been open to those people who ventured up the Nile into Nubia.

The temples, situated south of the Tropic of Cancer and not far from the Sudan frontier, are so remote that few tourists or travellers saw them before news that they might be lost for ever stirred more to the effort. As the south-bound boat takes a slow bend in the Nile both temples creep into view, at first more mysterious in their isolation than impressive in their size, but growing every moment as the boat approaches, until at last they stand revealed, alone, colossal and unforgettable, with the river of sand flowing between them down to the water's edge. They and their setting are one and inseparable. It is as though the defied Ramses had for a moment made finger-tip touch with the creativeness of God when he set his idols to keep watch on the frontier of his world.

Ramses, who reigned for sixty-six years from 1298 to 1232 B.C., had an egomaniac passion for preserving for ever the record of his name and deeds. He used his finest craftsmen on the temples of Abu Simbel which are the greatest of all his monumental creations. It is only for the record that one gives their dimensions. The façade of the great temple is 119 feet broad and over 100 feet high and formed like a pylon. The temple is 200 feet in depth. The four colossi of Ramses, hewn out of the cliff against which their backs are placed, are 65 feet in height. The temple of Nefertari is 90 feet long and 40 feet high and its six statues are 33 feet tall. In a world now accustomed to mammoth structures, in which cities like New York climb into the air as though no longer earth-bound, measurements can belittle what they intend to extol; there is always something bigger. Abu Simbel is big; big enough not to require a conjuring trick of memory to enhance its stature with the recollection that it was created three thousand years ago by straining human muscles on simple tools. It stands in its own right superb and, in the first face to face revelation of it, breath-taking in its magnificence. For – and this is the characteristic that transcends dimensions – the colossal figures are carved from the living rock of the cliff-face with precision and delicacy. One statue has been decapitated and its head lies at its feet, but the other three look down identical in shape and gentleness of expression, each with a trace, and the same trace, of a smile on the lips.

The lesser temple which has three statues of Ramses and his queen Nefertari on each side of the entrance is equally superb in its workmanship. Both were carved from the sandstone cliff which at the time sloped down to the river so that the rock had to be cut away at the base for 90 square feet and excavated to that level to provide sufficient area for the façade of the great temple. The stone is pale yellow in colour and soft in structure except where hard reddish brown strata intrude.

The smaller temple near to the water's edge, is dedicated to the goddess Hathor and is a memorial to Ramses' queen. The greater temple was dedicated to Ammon of Thebes and to Re-Harahkte of Heliopolis, the leading deities of Egypt during the nineteenth dynasty, but Ptah of Memphis and the deified Ramses were also worshipped there. It is approached by a terrace adorned with rows of captives and a balustrade. Above the colossi of the façade is a cornice of carved monkeys. The statues show the pharaoh seated and wearing the double crown of Egypt, with small figures representing members of his family carved against his legs. The roof of the temple itself is supported by eight square pillars, against each of which stands a beautifully executed figure of the king in the guise of Osiris. This hypostyle hall, excavated out of the solid rock, achieves grandeur by its excellent proportions, and its sombreness is relieved by its decoration and design, which display a delicacy and energy of movement that one could hardly expect from such rough material. The walls are covered with spirited pictures of events in the reign of Ramses, the most notable of which, depicting Ramses engaged in the Syrian campaign against the Hittites, has a freedom and vigour that is truly great art, and is full of remarkable detail, such as the charioteer with his reins tied around his waist to free his hands to draw his bow. On another wall there is a picture of the same campaign showing all the bustle and excitement of the camp. There are hundreds of casual inscriptions on the walls of great value to the historian. For the most part these are the scribbles of the mercenaries in Egyptian armies that warred in Nubia through many centuries and they carry history in episodic fashion right through to Greek and Roman times. There is a long gap in the records when the temples were covered with sand until we come to the grave of Major Tidswell, who died in 1884 during the British expedition up the Nile and was buried at the south end of the façade near the last colossus.

The orientation of the great temple imparts to it a remarkable characteristic. The longer axis of the interior runs due east and west so that the first ray of the sun at dawn strikes straight through the hall to light the altar with awe inspiring effect. 'Appreciation necessarily contains a subjective element,' wrote Sir Mortimer Wheeler, 'but anyone with a normal sensibility who has seen these gigantic seated figures of the pharaoh grow almost organically out of the darkness, has seen the first shaft of sunlight strike into the mighty corridor within the rock and light for a passing moment the serried countenances of the god of the dead, has looked upon the face of Egypt with some new understanding. There is nothing in 3,000 years of Egyptian civilization comparable with this. It is the veritable entry into the underworld to which pharaonic Egypt gave so much of its thinking. We need not admire the fear and philosophy which inspired it, to admire Abu Simbel. It expresses, as only the great works of art and architecture can express, the shape of history. To lose it would be irreparable loss'.[1]

The Director General of U.N.E.S.C.O. reported in May of 1960 that the international experts consulted by the U.A.R. considered the safeguarding of Abu Simbel and Philae 'as the most important consideration under its commission', and in the sense that everything else to be done in Nubia could be undertaken with a reasonable degree of certainty, this was so. The U.A.R. Government and U.N.E.S.C.O. therefore signed a contract with the *Bureau d'Études André Coyne et Jean Bellier* for a

[1] *The Times*, July 7, 1962.

preliminary survey and detailed estimate for the construction of an earth dam and enrockments to protect the Abu Simbel temples where they stood.

Dr. Pierre Gazzola had already prepared plans and a model to show how the temples could be raised to a higher level out of reach of the High Dam lake but at the outset there was so much scepticism about his fantastic scheme that it was left for consideration only if Coyne and Bellier reported a protecting dam to be impossible of execution. Although they eventually produced a feasible plan, the cost of building a rock-fill dam high enough to hold the reservoir at its maximum and with space enough in front of the temples to give a view of them from the lake was estimated at $82 million. The porosity of the sandstone contributed greatly to the high cost, for the French engineers had not only to design a dam to hold the water at bay, but also to provide an elaborate grouting system and cut-off trench to reduce seepage through the rock. Even so, the scheme provided for pumping equipment, because the smallest quantity of water could cause damage, and the annual maintenance of the pumping plant was estimated to be $370,000.

Apart from the costs and the hazards, there was increasing aesthetic opposition as people realized how little of the beauty and spirit of Abu Simbel would survive the imprisonment of the temples in a dammed area. They are carved in the cliffs, part of a landscape sublime in its open emptiness, ready to greet the dawn of each day, and it was reasonable to ask whether, the documentation of the temples being complete, it was worth so great a sum to preserve them without their setting. Gazzola proposed to save both by raising the two rock masses enshrining the temples and then reconstructing the surrounding hill landscape to accord with the existing riverside setting so that the ultimate position of the temples would be the same in relation to the level of the reservoir as they were in relation to the existing course of the Nile. The visitor could still sail to their shore and walk over the terrace into the ancient portals.

When the U.N.E.S.C.O. General Conference met in November and December, the Director General submitted both plans, the Gazzola idea having been sponsored by the Italian Government and prepared in detail by the firm of Italconsult. It was estimated then to cost $60 million, substantially less than the French scheme. The conference asked the Director General and the U.A.R. to consult international experts, five of whom met in Cairo and recommended the Italian proposal. The U.A.R.'s Committee of Experts were still unhappy about lifting the fragile rock, weighing 300,000 tons in the case of the great temple, and suggested to the U.A.R. Government that Italconsult should re-examine some of the difficulties inherent in the project. The archaeologists were of the opinion that the rock would collapse when taken from its bed; and if the lifting failed, that would be the end of Abu Simbel. It worried them that the experts had not lifted by the method they proposed anything one-tenth the weight of the great temple and certainly had never lifted a temple carved from a sandstone cliff. But at last they were convinced. In January they agreed that the monuments should be lifted.

The Gazzola scheme involved lifting each temple on 250 hydraulic jacks a millimetre at a time a distance of 210 feet to the top of the hill behind them. The first difficulty it had to face was cutting the block containing each temple from the heterogeneous and cracked rock without breaking it. Italconsult proposed to remove the rock above the temple carefully and without blasting, and to cut vertical and horizontal cavities down the sides and underneath the temple in which reinforced concrete structures would be built. A front wall would be constructed to protect the façade during the lifting and a roof would link all the concrete side walls. The effect would be to create a very strong box in which the block containing the temple would be securely housed.

The problem of lifting was complicated by the fact that the distribution of the load on the platform would never be known because of the nature of the rock, the cracks in it, and the existence of the cavity composing the temple interior. The load had therefore to be trusted to the jacks, not the platform, and Italconsult proposed to control all the jacks in a fixed upward step of one millimetre, checking each movement electronically so that the failure of any one jack would stop the operation. At the same time, the perfect plane of the lift would be measured by a series of communicating vessels filled with mercury and composing a giant spirit level. After each 30 centimetres, the lift would be halted while prefabricated beams were put in place, so that when the whole operation was complete they would provide adequate foundations and the protecting walls could be withdrawn. The surrounding landscape would then be reconstructed. Italconsult wanted work to start on the Nefertari temple in the summer of 1963 and on the great temple a few months later.[1]

Before this stage was reached, however, considerable preparatory work was required. The U.A.R. Experts Committee reported in January 1961 that the first and urgent step was to consolidate the façades of the temples, and, while U.N.E.S.C.O. struggled to raise the money, the U.A.R. set contractors to work to conserve them, proceeding as though the scheme would certainly be executed. The Antiquities Department began clearing the sand from between the two temples, and various foreign firms surveyed the ground for the excavations, measured the effect on the sandstone of drilling and grouting and tested the rock in laboratories for porosity and permeability. On February 4, 1962, advertisements appeared in the British Press asking for tenders for raising the temples. They specified the excavation without explosives of 350,000 cubic metres of rock, hydraulic jacks with a lifting capacity of 450,000 tons, the boxing of the temples in 50,000 cubic metres of concrete, and the building of an artificial hill. The contracts should, in fact, have been signed in January and the date had been postponed to November. Every delay now meant an increase in the cost, for the later the date of completion the higher the temporary coffer dam would need to be to protect the work on the temples. In November, with still no sign of contracts, it was announced that the planned height of the coffer had been increased by 12 feet.

At this stage the Italian scheme died the natural death of all large enterprises for which there is not enough money. Its demise was foreseen by many people who had ideas of their own for the saving of Abu Simbel. None was more ingenious than that of

[1] An excellent description of this scheme, the ingenuity of which seemed almost worth the money, was given by Professor Gustavo Colonetti, President Honorary and Emeritus of the National Research Council of Italy, in *New Scientist*, April 27, 1961.

William MacQuitty, a Belfast film producer, who travelled down the Nile in 1962 and, thinking of Atlantis, the mythical sunken continent, got round to the idea that the temples could best be preserved under water. He did not let the matter rest in fancy. On his return home he secured the co-operation of Ove Arup and Partners who, in association with Fry, Drew and Partners, prepared a plan which MacQuitty submitted to the U.A.R. Government and which Edmund Happold described in *The Architect's Journal* of March 20, 1963. If cost had been the only concern, the MacQuitty scheme would have been adopted there and then, for MacQuitty estimated that the whole project, including restaurants, lifts and air conditioning, would be a mere $6,440,000 and the annual upkeep only $50,000.[1]

As Edmund Happold described it:

> 'Around each temple will be built a thin "membrane" enclosing clean water on the temple side and keeping it constantly at the same level as the Nile outside. This would result in the pressure on the membrane being balanced on both sides, so that the membrane could be a light and inexpensive structure. It would be of reinforced concrete, folded for stability against sudden differences in water level, wind forces, collision from river boats, and the like.
>
> 'There would be a walkaway along the top with lifts descending to galleries, built in the thickness of the folded membrane, from which the temples could be seen through windows set in the sides. From the galleries a tunnel would be set into the floor of the temple, along which sightseers could walk into observation rooms within the underground halls. Lighting, of course, would be required, and the galleries and tunnel would have to be ventilated, but an attraction such as this would draw tourists from all over the world.
>
> 'The water within the membrane would be purified by filtration, any unbalance being dealt with by adding acid or alkali. Micro-organisms would be killed by adding certain chemicals which would also enable them to be removed on the filters. The Candy Filter Company thinks there would be no major problem'.

The Paris correspondent of *The Times* reported on March 21

[1] Letter to *The Times*, July 16th 1963.

that 'it seems certain that little more than derisive attention has been paid to the scheme for immersing the temples in purified water . . . the idea of replacing a serious archaeological venture with what some saw as a sightseeing circus was apparently found shocking'. The translated vision of Atlantis was still-born and Mr MacQuitty was able to complain to *The Times* by letter in July that his scheme had not been considered.

Yet one scheme considered was as remarkable – if less Hollywood – as Mr MacQuitty's gold-fish bowl. It seemed as though the very air of Abu Simbel that had prompted Ramses II to his architectural wonderland was still working its magic on all who would try to save it. The new scheme was prepared by M. Albert Jaquot, member of the French Academy of Sciences, chairman of the French Committee on Soil Mechanics, and a well-known specialist who had executed big water-lifting jobs in the shipyards of St Nazaire and the basin of the Rance River, and it was submitted to U.N.E.S.C.O. by the French National Commission. In brief, the plan was to float the temples to the top of the hill.

M. Jaquot proposed to cut the temples from the rock with floating foundations beneath them. They would rise 206 feet as the High Dam lake filled and would then be moved 393 feet horizontally to previously prepared sites on the bank and the landscape reconstituted around them. It was estimated that the operation would cost $35 million, but it was rejected largely because many experts believed that the estimate would be greatly exceeded.

After Gazzola's jacking scheme, Mr MacQuitty's glass bowl and M. Jaquot's rafts, the proposal of the U.A.R. Government's consultants, the Swedish firm VBB, was the prosaic conception of cutting up the temples, moving them to a higher level out of reach of the dam reservoir, reconstructing them there, and then remaking the landscape. But in execution this scheme was as remarkable as the others, for it meant carving and re-assembling 300,000 tons of fragile sandstone with the precision of a jeweller, so that the damage to the visible rock faces would be negligible. The saws used for the cutting would be like cheese slicers – thin, serrated wires of intensely hard metal stretched taut and oscillated by machinery. The engineers would quarry down to within three feet of the natural ceiling and trench down behind the 'walls'. The temples would then be cut into slabs, the size and shape of which would be determined by the natural cracks and weaknesses of the stone. Each block would be numbered, waterproofed to prevent discolouration from the concrete, lifted by 30-ton cranes, reassembled, and the tiny cuts sealed with mortar the exact colour of the sandstone. Only one part of the finished job would be artificial: the floors of the temples would be new but exact replicas of the originals. Professor Emery, Britain's representative on U.N.E.S.C.O.'s Nubian Committee and the Experts Committees of both the U.A.R. and the Sudan, was convinced that it would be impossible to distinguish a single joint when the rebuilding was completed.[1]

This was the scheme finally adopted and put into execution.

A small coffer dam was first built around the temples, and steel scaffolding, heavily padded with felt and pre-stressed to avoid vibrations, was erected inside them to take the strain of the external work. In May of 1964 the work of cutting away the overburden of rock began. The temples will be rebuilt at the higher level ready for reconstitution of the site in 1969.

[1] Report in *The Sunday Times*, June 30, 1963.

CHAPTER SIXTEEN

The Pearl and Other Gems

Old boatmen on the Nile at Aswan tell the story of Anas el-Wogud, the king's favourite who fell in love with the Vizier's beautiful daughter, Zahr el-Ward, Rose Blossom. The Vizier opposed the marriage and sent his daughter to a fortified island, where she was shut away from the world. Anas travelled far and wide in search of her until a hermit in the desert directed him to the island, to which he was transported on the back of a friendly crocodile, and he rescued her, married her and they lived happily ever after. The tale is from *One Thousand and One Nights* and the island may be called by the boatmen Castle Island, or, more picturesquely, the Island of Anas el-Wogud. To most people, however, it is known as Philae, which is the Greek version of an ancient Egyptian name, and tourists who brave the heat of summer to visit its famous temple when the Nile is low behind the Aswan barrage will be told by the dragomen that the Osiris room in the temple is the bridal chamber of Anas and his Rose.

Philae is the most easterly of the islands in the Nile at Aswan, the remains of a granite shelf which is the start of the first cataract. It is small and lies close to the bank, with a narrow channel separating it on the western side from Bigeh, which is twelve times its size, and another island, el-Heseh, which is three times larger than Bigeh and is situated close to the west bank.

Bigeh was the sanctuary of the Nile itself. A bas-relief in the Philae temple shows the God of the Nile crouched in a cavern among the rocks of Bigeh, dispatching the fertilizing water to the river, a representation of the ancient Egyptian belief that the annual flood was the gift of the deity hidden under the river-bed. Both islands probably had temples from very early pharaonic times, but of these almost nothing remains, and the first mention of Philae dates from about 350 B.C., the period to which the oldest parts of the Philae temples belong. The building of the monuments now adorning the island was begun by Philadelphus and was continued throughout the Ptolemaic period and by the Roman emperors, Augustus, Claudius, Trajan, Hadrian and Diocletian. The Christians later built churches or converted temples for their worship.

The people on Philae were not converted to Christianity until about A.D. 550, so powerful was the cult of the goddess Isis in the minds of Greeks, Romans and the surrounding indigenous peoples. Philae became a centre of pilgrimage for the Greek and Roman worshippers of the goddess, whose importance by then transcended that of Osiris, the pharaonic god whose legend explained all ills and authorized all hopes. The body of Osiris was supposed to be buried on Bigeh which was his sanctuary, wrapped by decree in perpetual silence and forbidden to all people in order that the god could sleep in peace in his sacred wood. Isis, at once his wife and sister, belonged to the living gods, and on holy occasions her idol was taken from Philae by boat to Bigeh to preside over the solemn libations at the tomb of Osiris. On the island of el-Heseh there is a necropolis where the faithful were buried as near as possible to the tomb.

Philae, as befits an island dedicated to goddesses, was 'the pearl of Egypt' before the waters of the old Aswan Dam destroyed its setting. The temples of Isis and Hathor are exquisite sanctuaries with two noble pylons, and the hypostyle hall, with its eight columns has both splendour and beauty. The Greeks departed from the pharaonic naturalism in the use of colours, but only enough remains now to show how brilliant the colouring must have been. There are many monuments on the island: the ancient and elegant pavilion of Nektanabos, Hadrian's gate and the ruined temple of Augustus among them.

Before the building of the first Aswan Dam, a traveller coming out of the granite wilderness of Aswan could not fail to feel enchantment at the first sight of the island of Isis, with its temples surrounded by palm trees and mimosas and all reflected in the waters of the Nile. The creation of the reservoir meant that part of the buildings and the entire island disappeared from view from December to mid-summer, and each heightening submerged more until at last the cornice of the pylons was all that could be seen for nine months of the year. The palms and the mimosas died and the walls of the monuments were caked with slime. This is how it is today: a blurred vision of beauty visible to only the hardiest of travellers in the summer heat.

Even this much might not have been left to the world had not Gaston Maspero, Director of Antiquities at the time, after making copies of all the monuments and inscriptions, strengthened the foundations in order to save what he could when it was decided that the temples could not be moved. There was, not unnaturally, a great outcry against the British for sacrificing the beauty of Philae to the need for the barrage, but the two plans to save it were considered impracticable. The first, to build a high strong wall around the perimeter of the island, would have hidden the temples from all outside view behind a prison-like wall; the second, to dismantle and reassemble the monuments elsewhere, seemed too hazardous an operation at the time.

It is fortunate that the second plan was not executed, for the building of the High Dam has made it possible to restore much of the beauty of Philae as it was before the turn of the century. When the new dam is complete, Philae will find itself in the pool between the two dams and not in the reservoir, so that the water will be much lower all the year round and more than half of the height of the temples will be visible. It is therefore possible to hold back the water at this lower level by dams and pump the water from the lake so that the island can emerge in its entirety from the river.

It was obvious that something had, in any case, to be done, for Philae was in greater danger of destruction than ever before. It is now submerged only once a year in the reservoir, so that little harm is done by the rise and fall of the river, but under the system that will operate when the High Dam is finished, there will be movement of the water almost daily between the two dams as it is released from the High Dam to the sluices of the old. This constant washing of the temples could quickly erode and destroy them.

The Egyptians found the solution to this problem for themselves as early as 1955. Dr Osman R. Rostem proposed that barrages should be built to connect Bigeh and another very small island north-west of Philae and to connect both islands to the river banks, so that Philae would be contained safely within its own pool and sheltered between Bigeh and the rocky hills south of Shellal. No one has been able to improve on this scheme, for it means that Philae will emerge intact from the river, its walls will be cleaned, and in time the palms and the mimosas will again add their enchantment to the scene. The pearl of Egypt will once again be a pearl.

The Dutch Government undertook to have a survey of the plan executed at its own expense by the Nedeco Bureau of Studies in September 1960, and the U.N.E.S.C.O. General Conference was told in December that Nedeco considered the Rostem plan feasible and had produced preliminary designs. In January the U.A.R. Experts Committee likewise pronounced the scheme sound, commenting only that they favoured electrical pumping of the water from Philae lake. In April, President Kennedy, in a message to Congress, offered to finance the scheme with $6 million; it was estimated at the time to cost $5·5 million.

Thus Philae became the first of the great monuments to be assured of salvation, although the work cannot begin until late in 1968, when the High Dam is finished and the waters between it and the old Aswan barrage subside. The sleeping beauty of the Nile will be wakened by the kiss of $6 million, and the sun will warm her body into life and bring back the colour to her pallid cheeks.

As Abu Simbel and Philae are the unforgettably great among the monuments of Nubia, it is natural that success in saving them should set the stamp of victory on the campaign, but in the final count their salvation is being brought about by the application of large sums of money to engineering skill. The archaeologist and the architect have played their parts in the planning, but without modern machinery and the industrial talent of the age it would certainly have been impossible to save Abu Simbel in time. The scholars are, indeed, grateful to find an ally in the engineering sciences and have always been quick to apply new techniques and scientific knowledge to the problems of excavation and the analysis of results. What would the prehistorian do now without the laboratories to read in thousands of years the age of a bone or a stone? Yet it is pardonable in the Nubian campaign to draw a line between Abu Simbel, Philae, and the reconstruction of other monuments like Kalabsha temple, and the researches still proceeding in Nubia above the slowly rising water-line. The Egyptian Department of Antiquities had itself done most of the dismantling of temples and other monuments in its region, and now the removal of all the monuments that can be saved, including those in the Sudan, where the Dutch and Belgian Governments are dismantling the stone temples of Semna and Kumma, is completed or in hand. The work of survey, excavation and documentation on the other hand, will not be finished until the last moment, when the reservoir at its full height puts a compulsory end to it. Even then there will be much left undone, for no one can know what layers of history escaped the eye of the searcher, and in studies and laboratories all over the world the multitude of relics and records will be examined with microscopic attention for many years to come.

It will be some time before the full story of the discoveries made during the campaign will be known, for the scholars themselves have not yet fully analysed or discussed them. The U.A.R. Government found it necessary at the end of 1963 to remind the missions that they must let the Cairo Documentation Centre have at least photographic records of new finds and notes of the localities from which they came. Many of the missions regard their discoveries as secret until the definitive report has been prepared for publication and delivered to the Department of Antiquities either of the U.A.R. or the Sudan. In some cases, notably in the field of prehistory, the discoveries have little material existence, consisting of the scholar's interpretation and report of an agglomeration of minute items and the soil in which they lay, but they may in the long run prove to be more important to the reading of history than many more spectacular finds.

Some of the discoveries are known. Mention has already been made of Buhen fortress and town, where the Egypt Exploration Society excavated down to the twelfth-dynasty structure and was able to reconstruct on paper the fortifications of both the twelfth-and the eighteenth-dynasty periods. The excavations enabled Professor Emery to visualize innumerable facets of pharaonic life, even to guess at the characters of the various governors' wives by the layers of paint on the pillars of the palace unearthed from the debris, and the discovery of the skeleton of a horse at the lowest levels revealed that the horse had been known in ancient Egypt centuries earlier than anyone believed. It was possible to deduce where the Kushites broke through the walls and which way the governor's palace fell when it was fired at the eastern end. These and many other facets are part of the mosaic of history constructed from the ruins, but the broad pattern of the discoveries was that the military art of pharaonic fortification was more advanced than that of the Middle Ages in Europe, as, for example, in providing both a vertical and horizontal field of fire from the apertures manned by the archers. The fortress was a most elaborately arranged defence; attackers had to cross a deep, dry moat always in the line of the archers' fire, and if they did so, and successfully scaled the high walls, they found themselves in a narrow walled road running round the perimeter of the fort to a single outlet, again at the mercy of the bowmen. It follows that the Kushites who breached such defences were not primitive rabble but were themselves an organized military power. The most important discovery of all, however, was that the pharaonic occupation of Kush took place on the first occasion not in the Middle Kingdom, but 600 years earlier in the pyramid age, for seals with the names of the kings and typical pottery of the period were found at Buhen.

Sixty miles north of the Sudanese frontier, Professor Plumley and Dr. W. H. C. Frend, of the Egypt Exploration Society, excavated within the cliff fort of Kasr Ibrim, 200 feet above the Nile. They cleared an ancient church down to its floor level, and in doing so established the fact that the site had been a most important centre of Nubian Christianity and that the decoration of its granite columns, one of which was still in place, was not equalled in Europe for another six centuries.

'Lying amid soft wind-blown debris only two feet below the arch at the entrance to the crypt, the workmen found the huddled body of a Nubian bishop', Dr. Frend later wrote.[1] 'He

[1] 'The Arab World', Winter 1964. Journal of the Anglo-Arab Association.

was lying hunched up, his brown outer garment being covered by a shroud. There was a linen scarf around his neck, an iron pendant cross hung on his breast, while a chasuble-like garment of richly woven fabric covered his shoulders. Among the garments, however, Professor Plumley found two tightly rolled paper scrolls.

'These were unrolled by experts in Cairo Museum. They showed that the bishop had been named Timotheus, and they were the diplomas of his appointment to be bishop of the combined see of Faras and Ibrim in 1372. They are magnificent documents by any standard, each more than 16 feet long, one in Boharic, and the other in Arabic, illuminated manuscripts of exquisite calligraphy. The information they provided, however, was of even greater value. They showed that Christianity had not been snuffed out by Saladin's brother, Shams el-Doula, but had survived for another two centuries at least. A new page had been added to the religious history of the Nile valley'.

There were other discoveries at Kasr Ibrim, including the paved courtyard of what appeared to have been a vast Meroitic temple similar to that at Kalabsha. The expedition also found the well-preserved remains of a house of the mysterious X-group people, the only X-group house ever identified.

The history of Christianity in Nubia will certainly be enriched by the knowledge gained and being gained in the campaign, but it is unlikely that anything will be found as remarkable as the basilica at Faras West, on the very frontier of Sudanese Nubia, excavated by the mission of the Polish Academy of Sciences led by Professor Kazimierz Michalowski. The site, which had been known for half a century and partially excavated, was dominated by a dervish fort, known as 'the citadel', perched on the top of a mound. The suspicion of the original expedition that this was not a natural mound was strengthened by the survey made by Dr. Adams and Mr. L. P. Kirwan in 1960, and the following year Professor Michalowski removed the fort and cut a trench straight into the mound, like slicing into a round of cheese. He found himself at once in a basilica of red brick standing on sandstone, with its walls covered with paintings of still brilliant colour and inscribed in both Greek and Coptic script. The very first picture to be revealed on the end wall of a chapel was an exquisite painting of the Madonna and Child.[1]

More than 200 paintings, most of them belonging to the tenth and eleventh centuries have been uncovered, and they reveal that a flourishing school of Nubian peasant painting harnessed to the spiritual needs of the early Christian communities was at its zenith at Faras at that time. Many of the pictures are of traditional Christian scenes, such as the Nativity and the Adoration of the Magi, all with Nubian characteristics such as hump-backed Nubian oxen in the holy stable and the dark skinned people. Another striking picture shows Nubians descending headlong into hell, like the Gadarene swine. There are also secular paintings of local nobility, and the identification of some of them and of some religious personages, together with the clear pictures of customs and clothes of the period, adds immensely to the shadowy knowledge of early Christian peoples. Further, as the expedition carefully removed the frescoes from the walls for preservation in the Warsaw and Khartoum museums, they uncovered earlier paintings from the eighth and ninth centuries. It has not been possible to preserve many of them, but the records of some have been saved. Similarly, some of the masonry used in the building has pharaonic and Greco-Roman inscriptions, suggesting that a pre-Christian temple stood on the site.

One inscription consists of a list of bishops of Nubia, apparently incomplete only in the fact that names of the first four bishops, who were presumably the first to occupy the See after its conversion by missionaries from Constantinople in the sixth century, are indecipherable. The list goes forward to 1169, which probably dates the destruction of the community by Shams el-Doula, who sacked Kasr Ibrim, in Egyptian Nubia, and took its population into slavery. There are inscriptions in Old Nubian, from which the unwritten languages used in Nubia today descend, and in the immense task of copying and deciphering this mass of texts, the Polish expedition secured the help of Mr A. F. Shore, of the British Museum.

[1] It must have been an exciting moment of discovery. I happened to be in the field office at Wadi Halfa when the photograph of the Madonna painting was brought in and caught something of the feeling when Dr Thabit allowed me to see it. – Author's note.

The discovery of a nearby Coptic church built in 940 and numerous tombs of the bishops of the See, make Faras one of the richest finds not simply of the campaign but of recent times. Another remarkable discovery of Christian monuments was made by a Dutch expedition, led by Dr H. Klasen, of the Leydon National Museum, on the banks of the Nile near Abu Simbel. It consists of a Christian chapel of the seventh century which, according to Dr Klasens, was still being used as the desert sands slowly buried it. Again, many fine pictures were found in the chapel, and these have been removed by Dutch and Egyptian experts and mounted on canvas covering about 300 square feet. The Dutch expedition also unearthed a Nubian village of the second century, which had been preserved almost perfectly by the sand that covered it.

On the island of Meinarti in the Sudan, Dr Adams discovered the remains of an extensive Christian settlement, with eleven distinct layers of occupation. At level five there emerged one of those mysteries of history which will never be solved, for it seems that the entire population of the village at that time abandoned their homes, leaving all their possessions behind. They never came back, and only long afterwards, when the sand had covered their habitations completely, newcomers arrived and built upon the sand. As a result, Dr. Adams was able to unearth a rich haul of early Christian domestic objects in excellent condition.

The Scandinavian Joint Expedition located and excavated settlements, churches and thousands of tombs in the Sudan, shedding new light on the history of early man in Nubia by diligent amassing of the remains. One of its most remarkable discoveries was a number of figurines of unburnt clay depicting a mature woman and a young girl in the grave of a woman. These figurines are about 5,000 years old and belong to the period of the 'A' people.

In 1963, when the U.A.R. Antiquities Service was dismantling the avenue of spinxes at Dakka, their workers unearthed an entire temple, with some of the paint still fresh on the walls. In doing so they solved a problem that had troubled Egyptologists for decades during which they had found references to one of the most important temples of Egypt in the 15th Century

B.C. without finding the slightest trace of the temple where it should have been. It had been dedicated to Horus by the great Pharaoh Thutmosis III but the only temple in the area was that of Dakka, dedicated to Thoth by Nubian monarchs of the late Ptolemaic era. The Egyptian archaeologists had at last found the missing temple of Horus, which had been hidden under the stones of Dakka for 2,000 years. Yet another large temple was unearthed while excavations were taking place at a little rock-hewn chapel just south of Wadi es-Sebua.

There have been numerous other discoveries less spectacular than these, such as the New Kingdom tomb, roughly contemporary with Tutankhamen, discovered by the expedition of Chicago University under Professor Keith Seele, and these will no doubt find their place in the records of the great campaign of the scholars in Nubia. It is enough now to say, as the 1964–5 digging season starts, that only about thirty miles of Egyptian Nubia remain to be explored, although the teams are still at work elsewhere in the region. In the Sudan there are about 120 miles on both banks of the river southward from Gemai to the Dal Cataract where only one excavation is committed, to the University of California. This section is the least known of all Nubia, 'a veritable unknown country', as Dr Thabet described it, so much so that the archaeological problems concerned in its exploration are not fully understood. It is, however, known to be the toughest region to explore, because of the dearth of communications, the difficulty of supplying the team in the field, and the absence of manual labourers. The problem has not been eased by the fact that with the inundation of Wadi Halfa there is no base in Nubia from which the expeditions can work; they must base themselves on distant Khartoum. The region from Gemai to Dal will be the last to be flooded, being the farthest south, so that work can continue there until 1966 and in some parts perhaps until 1970. There is little reason to suppose that, with this time available, the work in Sudanese Nubia will go unfinished. The final words are with Mime Désroches-Noblecourt: 'The history of Nubia can at last be written'[1]

Great enterprises often have unforeseen results. The sprawling monster of a dam now being built at Aswan is itself a creative

[1] The U.N.E.S.C.O. 'Courier', December, 1964.

thing whose benefactions will in time reach out to the lives of the meanest Egyptians. It would have been a sorry matter if, in doing so, it had destroyed much of the stuff of ancient history and left the world of scholarship and the knowledge of men so much poorer. Instead it stirred to life the scholarly ambitions of the world and led to the mounting of a campaign which will itself be recorded as a wonder of the modern world and fill some hundreds of volumes before its tale is finally told. And this is how it should be. Man's journey into the future, even into space and perhaps ultimately into other worlds, is enlightened by the knowledge of his past.

PART FOUR

The Beginning of the End

CHAPTER SEVENTEEN

The Last Flood

The sun of Aswan smiled serenely on the climactic May of 1964. It was torrid but not torturous, perhaps out of respect for the grey hairs of Mr Krushchev who suffered it to celebrate the diversion of the Nile to which his money and men had made their contribution. He arrived in Alexandria by sea, smiling benignly, in the manner of a benefactor, on the enthusiastic people who lined the route to cheer him, and by the time he reached Cairo he was so greatly conscious of contemporary achievements like the High Dam and the sputniks that he was bored and contemptuous of the great pyramids of Giza.

Day planes and night trains from Cairo were now filled with notables and Pressmen making their way to Aswan for the ceremonies. The finishing touches were being put to a new hotel, hastily completed for the occasion, even as the guests arrived to take their rooms, and at the river-side two houseboats which had been denuded of their tourists were moored to take the overflow. Tourists parties had been politely deflected from their course to by-pass Aswan because there was nowhere for them to sleep. The Cataract Hotels, both new and old, were reserved for Mr Krushchev, President Nasser and those who accompanied them.

The scene at the site was now complete and comprehensible to the onlooker. Handfuls of men worked here and there in the diversion channel but their diminutive labours could not disturb the sublime silence that enveloped it. It was rough but clean. The granite cliffs fell sheer to the floor. The rounded buttresses of the tunnels faced robustly upstream to Khor Kundi and the housing of the hydro-electric station stood squat, square and solid over the downstream exits. Standing on the rock roof of the tunnels one could see the arched chasm complete between the sand-blocks which, for only a little longer, held the Nile at bay.

There was still noise at the river as the dump trucks stored rock on the banks or dumped it in the water. The upstream coffer dam, constructed simultaneously from the east and west banks, looked like two arms straining but not quite able to touch. Along each arm an unbroken line of trucks, their gears grinding and engines roaring, moved ceaselessly to pour their loads of rock into the river. All that remained to be done for the completion of the first stage of construction was to close the gap in the coffer dam and destroy the sand-blocks on the diversion channel.

On May 13 the stage was set. Nearly 200,000 cubic yards of rock had been piled on the river-banks beside the coffer dam, and from each bank the loaded dump trucks stretched head-to-tail to the unfinished end, where six trucks stood in a line, backed-up ready to drop their loads into the river. Reporters, photographers, and television cameramen from all over the world crowded the ends of the dam overlooking the gap and on the banksides thousands of workers chanted their praise of President Nasser and the dam as they awaited his arrival. Groups impatiently broke through the cordon of police and advanced along the dam to swell the crowds at the edge, where the police tolerantly allowed them to stay and declaim with increasing hoarseness their rhythmic praise. One man, perched on the shoulders of another two in order to overlook his fellows, called his tribute which the crowd echoed, until every possible eulogy had been exhausted and the cycle began again. So the early hours passed while the Aswan sun climbed and beat mercilessly on the groaning Pressmen and the delirious, chanting claques.

President Nasser and Mr Krushchev, accompanied by President Sallal of Yemen, were by this time sailing on the yacht *Ramses* towards the coffer dam. They had come by plane from Cairo, paused to rest at the Cataract Hotel, and then boarded the yacht for the first ceremony, which consisted of dropping small inscribed pieces of rock in the river as they sailed through the gap in the coffer dam, as a signal for the closing of the gap. For some reason, which must have been as incomprehensible to Krushchev as it was to all other observers, President Sallal had also been asked to contribute a rock.

As the *Ramses* came into sight a great wave of sound from the masses of people on the banks enveloped the river and was pierced by the sirens of small boats which had congregated in the vicinity. The noise mounted in crescendo, was punctuated by a split second of silence as the three rocks were thrown, and then the world went mad.

Rockets on the banks fired pictures of Nasser and Krushchev into the sky, the wild roar of the crowd broke out afresh, and then all other sounds were engulfed by the noise of the 25-ton dump trucks whose powerful engines exploded into life and klaxons screamed in warning as the wheels began to turn. There was warning but no waiting: the six lined up at the edge of the dam backed straight to the river, raised their great backs and tipped the rocks without a moment's pause. The crowds scattered in all directions in the limited space, darting for their lives from the wheels that moved relentlessly upon them. To escape from the dam became a hazardous adventure, for the stream of loaded trucks advancing up the left side was duplicated by an even faster line of empty trucks racing down the right side and the people bumped and jostled each other in a grotesque dance as they ran, jumped and side-stepped their way to safety. Yet no one died; not even the television cameramen, loaded with massive tripods, cameras and sound-recorders who seemed at the moment to be purposely equipped for tragedy.

The *Ramses*, one might have remarked had there been time, sailed peacefully away to the south and swung-in to Khor Kundi. The three leaders were overtaken in the diversion channel by those Pressmen who were quick enough to make the traverse from the dam by car. President Nasser led the way through a tunnel and on emerging through the housing of the hydro-electric station at the other side, boarded a car with his guests and drove off through the cheering crowds.

The occasion had been dramatized to a great extent and the roaring lines of trucks that went to work with fearsome effect were more for show than necessity. Beneath the surface of the river in the gap the coffer dam was already closed and the river was beginning to rise slowly against it. What remained to be done was well within the capacity of the men and machines available and was, in fact, completed without using the fifty-four British 35-ton trucks, which, having played no small part in the enterprise, were hidden away in their garage for the duration of the Soviet visit.

The anxieties of the engineers were focused on the diversion of the river due to take place the following day. For the first time, all the work of preceding months, particularly the tunnels and the housing of the hydro-electric station, would submit to the pressure of the water, and the river itself, emerging from the channel, would need to rejoin its own valley at the level of the water there. The sequence of events would be the destruction of the upstream sand-block, the opening of the gates at the entrance to the tunnels and the destruction of the down-stream sand-block, and much depended on the timing of it. The event would be watched by the leaders of Russia and Egypt and, behind them, the entire world; at the very least, it would be a calamitous loss of face if the historic occasion were to fail by some minor bungle, even if no great harm were caused.

In the last twenty-four hours preceding the diversion there was little left to be done. Over 2 million cubic yards of water were pumped into the diversion channel, making a shallow lake which would act as cushion to the river when it broke in. The small charges of dynamite were already in place in the sand-blocks and in the last hours before the diversion, bulldozers carved a deep groove in the upstream sand-block to ease the passage of the water when the explosions fractured its surface. Only a small break was needed; the weight of the water would do the rest.

The rock plateau roofing the tunnels was converted into an extensive pavilion with gaily-coloured tenting, which is used in Egypt for all occasions from the celebration of a birth to mourning for the dead. Its forward edge above the tunnel entrances faced towards Khor Kundi and at a table there was the electric button by which Nasser and Krushchev would simultaneously signal the destruction of the sand-block.

As the roads to the site were closed to the public at 7 a.m. on the morning of the 14th, the 34,000 labourers at the dam and those people of Aswan who could get transport, were already thronging the hill-tops and ridges overlooking the channel in the early morning. The Press took their positions on the edge of the pavilion, the television and other cameramen fixing their equipment precariously above the tunnels, where a slip might send man or machine bouncing off the concrete casing to the bed of the channel 200 feet below. The invited guests, who included the entire U.A.R. National Assembly and all the Cairo ambassadors, began to take their seats in the pavilion shortly after seven.[1] Ministers and principal engineers assembled on the platform. Cages containing white doves were deposited on the concrete terrace above the tunnels inside the channel. Mr Krushchev and President Nasser, this time accompanied by President Aref of Iraq as well as President Sallal, arrived at 9.30 to the accompaniment of cheers and chanting from the multitude on the hills.

The chasm waited, hot and still, under the gleaming blue of a cloudless sky. Inside the pavilion the speeches, each with its translation into Russian or Arabic, nibbled the sweating hours away as speaker followed speaker, first the Minister for the Dam, then President Nasser, Mr Krushchev, President Sallal, and finally President Aref. The pavilion looked like the shadowy interior of an oven with glass sides and the audience like serried ranks of roasting chickens. To the listeners, their minds numbed by the heavy heat, words became meaningless incantations. The people on the hills endured the hours in the blazing sun without, it seemed, anyone fainting or falling from his perch, and when at noon President Aref made the valley resound with eloquent declamation of Arab nationalism they were still alive enough to chant in echo of his words.

Suddenly the long wait was over. There was silence as Mr Krushchev and President Nasser walked from the platform to the sunlit edge of the pavilion and, without further ado, together pressed the button. There was a dull explosion, a cloud of sand burst into the air from the block, rockets sent their pictures of the two leaders into the sky, and the doves fluttered dizzily from their cages. In a few seconds, before the air was clear, a trickle of yellow water crawled over the fractured sand-block and from the surrounding hills a great cry of 'Water! There's

[1] The ambassadors flew from Cairo at 5 a.m. in a special plane. One remarked wryly before boarding, 'It should be an interesting diplomatic situation if this plane crashes'.

the water!' filled the valley with triumph and more pride than the eloquence of any man could match.

The trickle of water grew into a stream and the sand crumbled, and the stream grew into a torrent and the block disintegrated. Workers, delirious with excitement ran across the crest to look at the tumbling water, were driven back as the crest itself broke away section by section, and yet returned again. The water, still yellow from the sand it carried with it, bubbled in the cauldron of the channel and, as it grew in strength, thrashed the granite walls fiercely and scrambled up the channel to the tunnels. The gates were raised and it rushed through to the downstream side, its torrent sweeping away one of three poor foolish men who had climbed on to the hydro-electric station for a better view. Another explosion shattered the downstream sand-block and the Nile, its flow freed by the opening of the sluices on the old dam, seemed to stretch an arm through the sand and draw the coursing water to it. Only half an hour after Krushchev and Nasser pressed the button the Nile was diverted.

During the excitement of that half-hour men from the hills broke the police cordons and invaded the pavilion, feeling no doubt, and justly, that they who had laboured for the day had the right to witness it. They pressed with increasing force on the front ranks, who were in danger of dropping over the precipice into the frothing yellow water below. The pressure only eased when President Nasser and Krushchev moved towards their car, and then everyone, invited and uninvited alike, were caught in the chaotic movement of escape from the pavilion, only to be swept by the human current at last into the sunlight and the greater pandemonium of bus, truck and car.

Peace came to the scene eventually, and in the evening it could be seen in all its silent splendour. The water was everywhere still, behind the coffer dam, in the river proper, and in the diversion channel. The tunnels and the hydro-electric housing were totally submerged and only little tongues of sand remained of the upstream and downstream blocks. The diversion of the Nile was visible and complete.

The subsequent ceremonies of President Nasser and Mr Krushchev seemed simple formalities after this great climax.

Together they went to see the last rocks dumped in the gap in the coffer dam, and later, when sand had consolidated its surface, they drove along its crest over the river. They unveiled a tablet on the column erected to commemorate the start of the work in 1960, this time to mark the diversion of the Nile. (Two more tablets remain to be inscribed: for the completion of the dam and of the hydro-electric works.) They banqueted together and presented medals to engineers and workers and returned to Cairo via Luxor, where Mr Krushchev was induced to have a grumpy glimpse of a few more pharaonic wonders.

Eighteen thousand Russians, the Egyptian engineers and 34,000 labourers remained behind with the rock and the river. It was their achievement that the world watched at Aswan, for they had laboured hard and long, latterly by day and night in one of the hottest regions on earth, to complete the first stage of the dam on time. Now once more they faced alone new years of work, and without a moment's pause they began again, this time for another long haul to 1968 when the dam is scheduled for completion. With the confidence born of success they said that they would finish the job by 1967.

It was not to be wondered at that Mr Krushchev gave a fortnight of his precious time to Egypt in order that he might savour with President Nasser the maximum public expression of triumph. The victory over time and the river was no less because in the beginning Russians and Egyptians had, from inexperience of the association, made many of their own difficulties. The two leaders could, as it were, look at the work of their hands and rejoice, for it was by their joint wills that men and machines had come together at Aswan. Nasser dared to proceed with this mammoth enterprise costing more than $1,120 million when it seemed beyond the capacity of his struggling state, and Krushchev staked $308 million on a hazardous undertaking when the Anglo-American offers of aid were withdrawn.

The plump flesh of Krushchev may have wilted in the Aswan heat but his spirit must have chuckled itself to sleep at the end of each day of celebrating. The arms deal with Egypt in 1955 and the High Dam were the two master-strokes of policy that brought Soviet influence back into the Arab Middle East and poked a probing finger into the heart of stirring Africa. Of these two, the High Dam was a victory bought at such a bargain price that he must have decreed perpetual candles in the Kremlin before the secular ikons of Dulles and Eden who made it possible.

So far Russia has undertaken to contribute about 308 million dollars to the building of the High Dam. The figure may increase before the work is finished and Nasser may yet be compelled to default on the re-payments, but even so, Russia will have paid a small price for all the benefits gained in the opinion of the developing countries. The contribution, repayable at 2½ per cent, has been spent almost in its entirety on Soviet technicians and Soviet equipment at prices that must have been profitable to the Soviet State, and the Aveling-Barford trucks, the Swedish drills, the Rustom-Bucyrus excavators, and the Dunlop tyres, were all paid for with badly needed sterling from the Egyptian pocket.

Further, the Russians were given a German design for the dam, prepared by the Hochtief-Dortmund combine and approved by an international board of consultants of the highest reputation, and this is still the basic design despite Soviet modifications. And, finally, 95 per cent of the decisive work of the first stage has been done by Egyptians.

This is not to belittle the greatness of the achievement so far; both Russians and Egyptians have done a magnificent job. But Russia has been able to sell to the world the idea that it is a Russian dam and this is far from true.

Ironically, the one place where Soviet glory burns least is in Egypt itself. Despite the rockets that fired Krushchev's portrait into the air, the laudatory remarks in speeches, the banners and slogans in praise of Russia at every few yards of his progress through Egypt, it is hardly possible that Krushchev and his entourage failed to see that he had been used on this occasion to the greater glory of President Nasser. He may, as one of the supreme world leaders, have viewed his state visit as a demonstration of the important position of influence he has gained in the Middle East, but this was not how Arabs recorded it. It was for them a patent demonstration of the power of Nasser that the Soviet leader could be summoned to Egypt. His speeches sought to educate the Egyptians in the way of Soviet thinking and policy but made no headway against Arab nationalism or Islam. The moment his back was turned, President Nasser agreed with President Aref on a plan for unity, which Krushchev had belittled, and Aref made it clear that he still had no intention of having truck with Iraqi communists. It was often a sombre Krushchev who stood beside the smiling and triumphant Nasser.

All this was possible because the Arabs regarded it essentially as Nasser's triumph. They are grateful for all Russia has done, particularly for Russian help in weakening the power and influence of the West, but they believe that they have exploited the self-interest of Russia for Arab ends and are anxious that Russia should not achieve a dominant position for itself. Nasser knows that for the time being Russia has fewer inhibitions than the West in supporting him, and for that reason he can travel for some time alongside Soviet policy; he knows that in present circumstances he must be tactful in relation to Russia, to which he owes much; but he also knows that he can rely on the support of Arab nationalists when he exerts his independence of Russia. Neutrality between the world *blocs* is a schizophrenic concept for them; on the one hand it is a cynical exploitation of the politics of aid and they commend Nasser when he is successful in it; on the other, it is a sincere faith in the integrity of the Arab world as it stands and struggles apart.

Krushchev may not have known all that happened during his sojourn in Egypt. As he drove at Nasser's side through the streets of Egypt the people shouted only in praise of Nasser until at last members of the security forces went ahead calling on them to remember their guest. The Egyptian always spoke of 'our dam', of 'our achievement', just as the bus driver, politely reprimanding his two insensitive English passengers, said he had not believed that *the Egyptians* could do it. He never mentioned the Russians.

There was one notable absentee from the celebrations: President Abboud of the Sudan.

The Sudan will also be enriched by the High Dam, for it has the guarantee of water for existing and new areas of cultivation.

The U.A.R. Government has estimated that as a result the Sudan will be able to treble its agricultural income and have new sources of power from the hydro-electric station at the dams it is building on the upper Nile.

It is the country, Egypt apart, most closely interested in the dam both now and in the future, and if the canal is cut through the southern swamps to free the White Nile – a scheme which, in its dimensions and problems will go far to rival the building of the dam itself – it can only be done by agreement between the Sudan and Egypt. The Governments are collaborating at present, in discussion of the swamp scheme, and in a Joint Technical Committee which is studying methods of restoring communications disrupted by the High Dam.

The coffer dam blocking the Nile at Aswan has already halted the steamer service that linked the two countries by barring access to the river port at Shellal, from which the boats plied to Wadi Halfa. As Wadi Halfa will itself be submerged, both Nile ports will soon disappear and need to be replaced if river traffic is again to start on Lake Nasser. The Joint Technical Committee is facing this problem and the U.A.R. Government allocated £E2,300,000 in its 1964–5 budget for its share of the cost.

The Egyptian port will be sited at Khor Kundi at the terminus of the new railway from Shellal, which has so far served as a supply route to the dam site. The terminal buildings will be high above the water and lifts will take the people and cargo to and from the boats. The Sudan port will be built in the vicinity of submerged Wadi Halfa and the railway laid by Kitchener for the reconquest of the Sudan last century, which runs from Halfa through Dongola to Khartoum, cutting off a great loop of the Nile, will be rerouted at its northern end to serve it. The Sudan authorities are meanwhile planning a passenger service by sea from Port Sudan to Port Said. Until this begins, or the service on Lake Nasser is operating between the two new river ports, the only way to travel between Khartoum and Cairo is by air.

The lake will also submerge the telephone cable route between the two countries and this will be replaced by a radio link. The technical committee is therefore preparing plans for permanent telegraph and telephone connection.

In the circumstances, the Sudan Government might have been expected to share in the celebrations at Aswan. This was far from the case, and the goodwill manifest when President Abboud gave his blessing to the High Dam in 1959 – the final act of consent that made the enterprise possible – was obviously lacking.

Representatives of the other riparian states were also absent from the ceremonies and this made the prominence given to President Aref and President Sallal all the more remarkable. President Abboud was himself heading eastwards for Pekin when the river was diverted, having declined President Nasser's invitation on the grounds of state visits arranged to Pakistan, India and China. Such poor politeness was doubtless intended, for the date of the diversion had been known for a long time. The Sudanese leaders were offended once again by what they considered the offhand attitude of President Nasser to their special position in relation to the High Dam, being share-partners in the Nile waters and having sacrificed their town of Wadi Halfa to the building of it. Instead of the pre-eminent position President Abboud might have expected, he got a belated invitation, and by that time he had taken care to arrange his state visits. When he delegated the Minister of Irrigation in his stead, the Egyptians refused to accept him in that role, and the Minister, who had been invited separately in his own right, then refused to go at all because of 'shortness of notice and pressure of work'.

The celebrations were no sooner finished than the engineers and labourers resumed their work on the river. The task before them is formidable but not frightening by comparison with the work that lies behind them, and it is calculated that only half the labour force used in the first stage of construction will be required for the second.

The downstream coffer dam is complete and the main site of the work is now the half-mile stretch of still water lying between it and the upstream coffer which was a feature of the celebrations. They are sluicing ten million cubic yards of sand as a great mattress on the river-bed, and consolidating it stage by stage as they proceed by a system of vibration, using heavy steel rods that are engined and suspended in metal frames. (The system can be studied in miniature by shaking a pencil rapidly in a cupful of sand.)

Almost all the rock excavated from the diversion channel has been used in the coffer dams, so three quarries have been started in the vicinity of the dam to provide another 30 million cubic yards of rock for the rock-fill over the sand. The dumping of the rock is keeping pace with the laying of the sand, with the result that the strata forming the body of the dam are being constructed simultaneously. Anyone looking into the river at this stage of the work would only see a chaotic massing of stone on sand, bearing no resemblance to a building process or the orderly raising of a concrete dam, but there is neither carelessness nor chaos; every load is laid scientifically in accordance with the blueprints.

The core is being constructed of clay along the main axis and as it rises to its full height, the wings of the dam will be constructed of rock-fill on the banks until they merge into the hills on each side of the river and are pinned there. These wings will be so high that another thirty yards will be added to the height of the roof above the tunnels in the diversion channel. When all is finished and the concrete blanket is laid over all, a broad highway will be constructed along the crest of the dam.

The work of consolidating the river-bed by fabricating under the main axis of the dam the grout curtain which is the vital and unseen element in the structure, will not begin until the clay core is almost completed, because the borings by which the clay and cement grout will be pumped into the bed will be done from the core. The borings must be done in a precise pattern, with each hole generally five yards from its neighbours and in some places only three yards, and it would be difficult, if not impossible, to achieve such precision from barges. There will be the additional advantage that the weight of the clay core will help to compress and consolidate the sludge. Inside the core there will be three inspection passages from which the engineers who will eventually stand guard over the dam can inspect it for fissures or other weaknesses.

As work proceeds on the dam, engineers are installing the hydro-electric generators in the station built downstream of the tunnels in the channel. These hydro-electric generators, each with a capacity of 175,000 kw., were designed by the Leningrad Elektrosla engineers in 1961, and are among the biggest in the world, exceeding those of the hydro-electric stations, such as Kuibyshev, on the Volga. Five of them will be commissioned in 1967, providing an extra 2,500 million kwh., and by 1971 the total of twelve generators, two to each tunnel, will all be operating and producing 8,000 million kwh. In the following year boosting generators will bring the output to the maximum 10,000 million kwh. and double the power capacity of the country.

Finally, an emergency spillway will be constructed on the west bank along the line of a natural depression which falls away to the river downstream of the dam. There is no urgency for this work because its purpose will be to discharge surplus water from the Nasser lake if its level rises above the maximum permitted level of 590 feet, and this cannot happen until a year or two after the completion of the dam in 1968. The spillway will be controlled by a weir 420 yards long about a mile and a half west of the dam, which will be able to release just over 3,000 cubic yards of water per second.

These works will complete the complex structure of the High Dam, but they would be useless without the means to make use of its water and its power. The size and variety of the works associated with the dam are an undertaking as vast as the dam itself and will cost Egypt more than twice as much. About $238 million will be spent on the construction of the dam and $1,610 million on the power station, but the cost of the lines to carry the power as far as the delta will be $140 million and the agricultural developments for use of the water, including irrigation canals, land reclamation, roads, housing and all the public utilities required for the communities who will live on the new land, will cost over $560 million. There will be, in addition, a final bill for $56 million as compensation for the displaced people. Taking the dam, the hydro-electric station and the related development works together, the High Dam will cost about $1,162 million.[1]

. . . . .

[1] These are official U.A.R. figures given in 1963 and compare with $1,027 million as the total cost estimated in 1960. Unofficial figures put the cost much higher but they vary considerably.

When the engineers now speak of completing the dam in 1967 they mean it will have reached an elevation of 165 yards and then be able to provide the over-year storage by which the irrigation system of the Nile will be transformed, and dependence on the Nile flood, which has been a condition of life ever since people began to live in the valley thousands of years ago, will cease for ever. The dam will achieve its final form, even to the road along its crest, in the following year.

Although the grandeur of the old Aswan Dam will be diminished by comparison with the giant now being built four miles to the south, it will remain the directing 'brain' of the annual irrigation of Egypt, the difference being that it will control a predetermined flow of water instead of the erratic supply of the river. The High Dam is being built in its reservoir, which is being absorbed in the greater man-made lake now named Lake Nasser, and what remains of it between the two dams will fall to a low level when over-year storage starts and will henceforth rise and fall daily as water is released to it in accordance with the prepared plan. As there are no sluice gates on the High Dam, and can be none, the river will by-pass it through the diversion channel to the sluices on the old dam, which will regulate the supply to the fields and farms of Egypt.

Lake Nasser is now partly formed, because the upstream coffer dam is storing an additional 5,000 million cubic yards of water from the 1964–5 flood and will continue to impound part of the annual surplus, until completion of the edifice in 1967 and the beginning of over-year storage of an additional 10,000 million cubic yards of water. The 5,000 million cubic yards of the 1964–5 season will be enough to reclaim 250,000 acres and convert half a million acres from basin to perennial irrigation. The acreage of land for reclamation or conversion will increase year by year to its maximum of a million acres reclaimed and 700,000 basin acres converted, for which enough water should be available by the time of the 1966–7 flood. How swiftly the Government can obtain for the nation these benefits of agriculture depends now on the speed with which the canals and irrigation ditches are provided, and the work on these, which has been under way since 1962, has been intensified since the completion of the first stage of the dam.

The new land and the extension of the perennial irrigation system will increase the irrigation area by about 25 per cent, which is a phenomenal increase in the wealth of a country which needs to exploit every inch of its cultivable land, but the ultimate benefits of the High Dam will extend far beyond this. The most important advantage will be that, for the first time in the country's long history, there will be absolute certainty about the water available for each and every crop in summer and winter, and this knowledge will enable the Ministry of Agriculture to plan in advance the products of the land in proportion to the needs of the Egyptians themselves and the best possible export opportunities. The combination of additional water, certainty of quantity and, therefore, the possibility to use it to the best possible advantage, will not only increase the produce from the land but alter the pattern of agriculture itself. For the first time, for example, Egypt will be able to put down a million acres to rice and the dependence of the country on cotton, the value of which has diminished with the advent of synthetic fibres, will be reduced.

There will, in addition, be complete protection against the high floods, which means that the Department of Irrigation will be relieved of the responsibility for guarding and strengthening the river embankments each year. Quite apart from the danger of a disaster, the river in too high spate always causes damage to standing crops by the infiltration of water through the dykes and thousands of watchmen are employed to guard against this damage. The savings in men and money by eliminating this annual problem will be considerable. Indeed, the change in the régime of the Nile, the control of its flow all the way northwards from Aswan, will touch the life of the country closely at almost every point and effect many minor benefits. Even the use of the river for navigation will be improved. It is estimated that the increase of the national income will be over £E250 million a year, or enough to pay for the dam and its associated works in less than two years.

The potential development of the country's power resources as a result of the dam is almost too great to estimate at the moment. The yearly output of 10,000 million kwh. from the hydro-electric station is equal to five times the output of the station at the old Aswan Dam and double the total electric power supply of the country, but, even so, it is only the beginning of the story. For example it would take about 2·5 million tons of *mazout* to produce the equivalent amount of electricity from a thermal power station, which means that the station eliminates the need for this oil fuel. By regulating the water pressure downstream, the dam will double the capacity of the hydro-electric plant at the old dam, and, similarly, by guaranteeing a head of water at the barrages on the Nile it will improve them for the production of electricity and perhaps make it worth-while to construct more barrages solely for power purposes.

The extent to which Egypt will benefit from these new resources will depend on the wise planning of industrial development but it seems beyond question that the 'rebirth' of the nation, the target of Nasser's revolution, is made possible by them. Nasser's revolt was staged as much against a stagnant economy as against a reactionary ruling class, and as he realized from the outset that the improvement of the lot of the common people required an immense increase in national production as well as a redistribution of wealth, and that agriculture alone could not provide it, the industrialization of Egypt was an essential element in his plans for progress. The expansion of industry in turn depended on the creation of new sources of power, and these too are being created by the High Dam.

The existence of power is already stimulating the search for minerals and other raw materials that can be exploited. The existence of iron ore of high grade and in large quantities has been known for centuries and is now the material of a steel industry, workable coal seams have been discovered in Sinai, and the newspapers have made frequent claims to the discovery of other minerals. It may well be that Egypt has more raw materials available for industrial exploitation. Even if this is not so, however, it is evident that the manpower of Egypt can add more to the national wealth by working in industries which might, in other countries, be considered uneconomic, because the value contributed to the product will be greater than can be added in agriculture, which is already excessively over-manned and costly to expand. To declare the industrial objectives of present-day Egypt to be uneconomic and wasteful is to condemn the country to stagnation and ultimate decline.

It is appropriate that the Nile, by whose grace and benefactions Egypt became the first among the nations of the world and has existed ever since, should adjust its role to the needs of the twentieth century, providing power for an industrial state as abundantly as it always provided water for agriculture. The change started, it is true, when the first turbines began to turn at the old dam and the first current flowed to Kima, but the hydro-electric station at the High Dam will so magnify the contribution that one will then justly think of the river as the source of power. A cable route from the dam will take the power through four transformer stations at Aswan, Nag Hamadi, Minia and Cairo, right into the delta, and in due time, with the flow of the river steadied by Lake Nasser, new generators along the Nile will give power to every inhabited corner of the land. Even the *shadoof*, the *archimedian screw* and the *saqia*, those living antiquities on the banks of the Nile which for thousands of years have helped the farmers to make more use of the river water, will be condemned to extinction or the museum and be replaced by electrically driven pumps.

All this presumes that pessimistic views of the storage possibilities of Lake Nasser, based on calculation of evaporation or theories that water will be lost through subterranean channels, are proved wrong. With regard to evaporation, the High Dam laboratory, after continuous tests, is convinced that the official estimates are correct. Hydrologists discount fears of loss underground.

Some of the laboratory tests have been concerned to discover whether evaporation can be reduced by the addition of a harmless chemical to the Nasser lake, a system by which it was hoped that Egypt could save about 5 million cubic yards of water, or nearly as much as the total storage of the old dam. Tanks of water were put out under controlled conditions and the loss measured and compared with the loss when chemicals were added under the same conditions. Although it was demonstrated that evaporation was reduced, it is very unlikely that the system can have any value to Lake Nasser. A U.N. commission has studied it in Israel, Australia and the United States and it has been used at a reservoir at el-Obeid in the Sudan, but its value seems to be limited to small areas of water, where it reduces evaporation by about 22 per cent. When used on big stretches of water the wind drives the chemical into one area and the need for frequent respreading makes the system too costly to be worth-while.

Eventually the supply of water at Aswan will be much greater than it is now, for the building of the High Dam modifies but does not exclude earlier plans for developing the Nile as a whole, and these plans include cutting a canal through the Sudd, the swamps of the Southern Sudan, where half the flow of the Nile is lost. The canal would substantially increase the supply in what is now the low season and would be of importance to Egypt even after the Sudan had taken its share of the water. The Nile Waters Joint Technical Committee is once again reviewing this project, which has been the subject of study by experts at various times since 1904[1].

The U.A.R. Government has never assumed that the High Dam was in itself the answer to all its economic problems, as some critics have tended to assume. They have always regarded it as the greatest single project, which would buy much needed time for national development, both in extension of the country's agriculture and by powering industrial expansion from its hydro-electric station. For that reason they evolved in 1960 a development plan for ten years, the time required to obtain most of the benefits of the dam. The progress of the country might reasonably be visualized as a jig-saw puzzle, with the dam as a central piece touching at some point almost all other projects and being assembled slowly over many years. The reclamation of large areas of desert and swamp between Cairo and Alexandria has already been started under the second part of the development plan and it is reckoned that with the High Dam contribution there will be water for cultivation of a million and a half acres. This estimate has been criticized as excessive and there is no doubt that it is indeed very big, but Egypt can 'borrow' water for years to come from the Sudan in

[1] The Committee resumed discussion on the Sudd scheme in July 1964.

accordance with the Nile Water agreement.[1] The Wadi Rayan scheme, which was first mooted in the eighties of last century and was once advanced as a rival to the High Dam scheme, will one day have its place.

Not all the major projects are directly associated with the river, however. One major plan which was launched almost simultaneously with the dam, depends on supplies of underground water in the desert west of the river. Since 1960, hundreds of workers, supervised by engineers and geologists, have been reclaiming land in a chain of depressions consisting of the oases of el-Kharga, Dahkla, Farafra, Bahariya and Siwa, using water from artesian wells. This region was fertile in Greek and Roman times, and Roman wells in the Kharga and Dahkla oases are among 120 wells now in use. The New Valley, as it has been named, has an area of about 35,000 square miles and the U.A.R. claims that about 300,000 acres can be irrigated indefinitely from the underground water. The present scheme is designed to reclaim 100,000 acres, of which nearly half are now said to be either producing crops or being prepared for cultivation. The oases have been linked by new roads and the New Valley capital, at ancient Kharga, has been rebuilt to house the workers on the project.

Another major project, estimated to cost nearly as much as the High Dam, concerns the Qattara depression in the western desert, where Allied troops took cover at the time of the battle of Alamein. The project was first mooted by Dr John Ball, of the Egyptian Desert Survey, in the twenties and was examined by the government shortly afterwards. Now, after years of intermittent study, the U.A.R. Government has sought W. German help in planning it. The depression, also in the western desert, is about 10,000 square miles in extent and has an average depth of about thirty-five yards below the level of the Mediterranean, which is forty miles to the north. The intention is to bring the water of the Mediterranean into the depression and to create another great hydro-electric station capable of producing

[1] The U.A.R. can 'borrow' just under 2 million cubic yards of water from the Sudan share until 1977. One British firm has contracted to supply 364 trawler-tractors, worth $8 million, for this scheme – an indication of its size.

3,200 million kwh. As the Qattara depression is only fifty miles from the New Valley oasis of Siwa, it is linked to that scheme in the desert development.

The progress of Egypt is beyond question and looking into the future one can visualize that it will have greatly changed for the better a decade from now, when many of the current developments will bear fruit. The manifest defects, such as lack of sufficient manpower, administrative inefficiency and often inaccurate appraisal of what the country needs, will mar the pattern of change and give less return for the expenditure of men and money than might be possible. Nevertheless, a great deal will be achieved, and the expanding middle class and rising living standards will in time help the country to overcome its problem of population growth. It is already noticeable that the middle class, a phrase used loosely in Egypt to describe professional men, army officers, higher grades of officials, technicians and workmen who have risen above the labouring rut, are having less children as they struggle to preserve for themselves and their families the standards they have with difficulty achieved. This social evolution is encouraged by the Government as an essential corollary of its development programme; for example, birth control pills were imported in large quantities in Egypt as soon as they came onto the international market.

The darkest shadow over this promising future is the problem of finance, for the massive development programme is a perpetual strain on the country's economy, despite Russian and other foreign credits and the vital yearly supply of American wheat against Egyptian currency which is turned into direct aid. The financing of the revolution has been described more than once as something of a mystery and it has certainly imposed a relentless search for funds. Taxation was increased in a decade to levels that Britain took a century to reach and the nationalization of industry and commerce against fifteen-year Government bonds, which in some cases have never been issued and in any case have little or no market value, has come close to confiscation. Profits have disappeared into the hungry maw of social and industrial development. The importation of luxury goods and many semi-necessary consumer goods has been stopped and travel abroad for Egyptians has been cut to the minimum, but neither these measures nor foreign aid, or the income of the Suez Canal, have overcome the chronic shortage of foreign exchange. The situation has not been eased by President Nasser's determination to pursue the Arab revolution by means which have brought him into conflict with other countries, thus limiting the help he might have got for them, and have involved him in a costly military campaign in Yemen. On the face of it, the cessation of foreign aid or severe restriction of it, would have disastrous effects on the programme of progress. But if Nasser can hold his course for another decade, he will be recorded as the greatest Egyptian and the builder of his country. If and when that story is told, the High Dam will have its place as the turning-point of modern Egyptian history.

Whether these notable efforts for the material well-being of man succeed or not, the great River Nile will never again be the same in Egypt after 1967. Its waters will no longer burst through the sluices of the old dam and fill the Egyptian channel with rich, brown water. The annual flood, the miracle' that through the ages has meant life to the people of Egypt and to this day is still watched in wonderment even by urban workers in Cairo, will not be seen again from that year forward and for ever. The tributaries will lose themselves in Lake Nasser and thereafter it will be by man's will, not God's, that water will be fed to the Egyptian fields.

The flood has a transcendent place in history for it contributed more than any other single factor in ancient life to the dawn of civilization and to the formation of the first nation-society known to man. It was to understand the flood, to predict its coming, to measure it, to control and use it, and to count its blessings in fruits and grains, that the primitive forerunners of the modern Egyptians were driven by necessity to form the elements of knowledge on which we depend to this day. They created a calendar of 365 days and by their observations of the heavens formulated a primitive but accurate astronomy; to measure and mark they began the science of mathematics, to count, the first system of accountancy, and to no small extent the need to record hastened the evolution of modern writing; in order to live together on the confined river-banks, they learned to build and in doing so invented tools and architectural methods; and because the Nile demanded co-operation, tribal frontiers blurred and vanished slowly in a unified state. The flood has meant so much to the Egyptians and all mankind that it is hard to think of any event more remarkable in recent times than that last Nile flood flowing past Aswan to Cairo and the sea.

Those gods of the river worshipped by the ancient Egyptians seemed conscious of the dramatic moment and angered that man should at last be able to limit their powers. The river had been diverted only a few weeks when the Roseires gauge reported to Aswan and Cairo that the greatest flood of this century was pouring down the Blue Nile to storm the half-formed defences of the new dam, and there ensued weeks of anxiety, exceeding any experienced during the first stage of construction. The danger was greater than that of 1946, not only because of the size of the flood but because the old barrage could not be used to hold the peak as it was on that occasion. Something was bound to be sacrificed, no matter what the decision: either damage to crops and villages by letting a great part of the flood through, or the destruction of the coffers on the High Dam by holding too much of the flood.

So immense was the volume of water coursing down the valley when the flood reached Aswan, that to use the old dam as in 1946 was now out of the question, for this would only hazard the barrage itself without reducing the force of the flow on the defences of the High Dam upstream; indeed it might endanger them further by raising the level of the lake too far. The safety of the coffer dams could best be achieved, of course, by letting the high flood flow freely through the new diversion channel, but as the flood could not later be held by the barrage downstream, the damage to the villages and farms of Egypt would be immense. There was, in short, no safe way of holding so great a volume of water, and the inevitable decision was a compromise to reduce the damage to the countryside as much as possible without allowing the coffer dams to be destroyed.

The conferences of the Russian and Egyptian engineers at this stage were grimly serious. The only action that could be taken was to close some gates in the tunnels of the diversion channel, which would have the effect of reducing the flow onto the old barrage and the countryside to the north, but would at the same time build up the lake behind the upstream coffer. But how many gates should be closed? The Government, which had its people and crops at stake, wanted as many closed as possible; the Russian engineers, who were unwilling to see the slightest abnormal risk imposed on the rock-fill coffer dam, wanted all the gates to stay open. Crops would grow again and village houses took no building, they argued.

At Kalabsha, forty miles to the south, a drainage port had been prepared to meet just such an emergency as this by drawing excessive water harmlessly into a depression in the desert before it could damage the dam, but on this occasion it was inadequate. The surplus flowed on past Aswan, washing away maize, sugar and vegetable crops and destroying villages on its way to Cairo, where it flooded streets. As in the case of the floods last century, the people took to the hills alongside the river, but a few lives were lost and much livestock. Villages as far north as the delta were evacuated in September and still there was no sign of the decline of the flood. But it could not now be long delayed. The Russian engineers therefore closed two of the gates in the tunnels to ease the pressure, and then partially closed a third. The Egyptian engineers believed that more gates could be shut and they, knowing more of their river than anyone in the world, may well have been right in concluding that the extra risk could be taken, as they were in 1946 with the old dam. The Russian engineers reckoned they had taken a big enough risk already, so, with these modest controls imposed, the Egyptian Irrigation Department stood guard on the whole length of the river. Their trucks were at the ready, their stocks of timber and ballast at peak, and the teams of engineers and labourers moved as fast as they could to the threatened banks of the river and canals.

It was not until the end of September that the flow began to fall, and, with the danger abating, it was possible to begin storing additional water. It is now hardly possible that the Nile can ever again threaten to destroy the work on the dam or damage the farmlands of Egypt. The flood of 1964 was its last fling. Although the annual flood will not entirely cease on the lower Nile until over-year storage begins in 1967, the amount of water held in 1965 will already be immense. In 1964 the High

Dam was doubling the lake of the old barrage and the enlarged lake will then be trebled in 1965.

On Elephantine Island in the Nile at Aswan can still be seen the ancient 'nilometer' which has measured since pharaonic days the height of each flood. A narrow staircase rises from the water through solid rock on which at each side are marked the measurements, and the ages of their use can be remarked by the change of script from the Egyptian, through the Greek to the Arabic and the French. Until hardly fifty years ago, when the old dam and the barrages on the lower Nile extended widely the system of perennial irrigation, it was vital that the river should record on the stone metre a rise of 16 *coudées*, about 28 feet, if Egypt were to avoid a year of severe want, because it was not until the flood rose above this point that the peasants could irrigate the basin land beyond the immediate banks. The dividing line was so sharp and inescapable that the agricultural taxes were waived if the sixteen *coudées* level was not passed.

In the most ancient of pharaonic times it was the custom of the Egyptians to placate Hapi, the God of the flood, by giving him in marriage a beautiful virgin who was thrown alive to him and the crocodiles from a sacred barge. Since the disappearance of this barbaric custom during the Old Kingdom of the pharaohs, the ceremony of blessing the flood of the Nile has been preserved by throwing an elaborately dressed doll into the river from a gaily decorated boat, and in modern times, until the extension of perennial irrigation made the level less significant, the ceremony took place on the day when a new nilometer at Rodah island, in the Nile at Cairo, recorded the level of 16 *coudées*. Now the Nile *fête*, *el-Waffa el-Nil*, takes place on August 22 each year.

With the end of the Nile flood in Egypt it will be a feast day without meaning and the time will come when Egyptian children will ask their parents what is the reason for the picturesque nonsense on the river. For Nasser has pledged, and rightly, that the annual ceremony of throwing the virgin-symbol to the Nile will not be abandoned. The High Dam will bestow its benefactions on the generations to come, but the flood which made it necessary was indirectly its creator.

Index